Longman
Geography
for GCSE

Authors
Ann Bowen
Roger Clay
Carmela Di Landro
John Pallister
Olly Phillipson

Series Editor Vincent Bunce

Contents

Addison Wesley Longman Limited

Edinburgh Gate, Harlow, Essex CM20 2JE, and associated companies throughout the world.

© Addison Wesley Longman Limited 1997

The right of Ann Bowen, Roger Clay, Carmela Di Landro, John Pallister and Olly Phillipson to be identified as authors of this work has been asserted by them in accordance with the Copyright, Designs and Patents Act of 1988.

First published 1997

ISBN 0582 293 936

Set in Caslon
Produced by Longman Asia Limited, Hong Kong
SWTC/01

The Publishers' policy is to use paper manufactured from sustainable forests.

Design and production by Moondisks Ltd, Cambridge

Printed and bound in the UK by Scotprint Ltd., Musselburgh.

Illustrations by Judy Brown, Tom Cross, Hardlines, Nick Hawken, Moondisks Ltd, Pat Murray/Graham Cameron Illustration, Oxford Illustrators

Picture research by Louise Edgeworth

We are grateful to the following for permission to reproduce photographs and other copyright material.

Ace Photo Agency/Benelux Press, page 152 above; Aerofilms, page 65; Heather Angel, page 83 centre; Barnabys Picture library, page 33; Big Pit, Blaenafon, Gwent, pages 142, 192 above; John Birdsall, page 116; Ann Bowen, pages 63 above, 85; Len Brown, page 197; Vincent Bunce, pages 16, 128 above, 183, 109, 203, 220; CAFOD, page 140; Chorley Handford, pages 29 below, 30 above, 43, 50, 193 above; Roger Clay, pages 8, 44, 49, 51; John Cleare Mountain Camera, page 25; Stephanie Colasanti, page 147; Colorific!, pages 17 (Enrico Ferorelli), 107 (Alon Reininger), 114 above (Steve Benbow), 167 (Heiner Muller-Elsner/Focus); Sylvia Cordaiy, pages 35, 42, (John Farmer); Reproduced from the Ordinance Survey mapping with the permission of The Controller of Her Majesty's Stationery Office © Crown Copyright (399582), pages 32, 33, 44, 49, 69, 79 left, 123, 126, 160; Daewoo, page 145; Ecoscene, pages 47 (John Farmer), 86 (Andrew Brown); Geographer's A-Z Map Company Ltd, © Crown Copyright, page 131; GeoScience Features Picture Library, pages 46, 72, 83 above, 83 below; Green & Black's, page 159 below; Sally & Richard Greenhill, page 139 below; Robert Harding Picture Library, pages 93 (Jeremy Bright), 95 above (J.H.C. Wilson), 193 below 216; The Hutchison Library pages 60, 121 (Edward Parker), 128 below, 171 below (Regent); ICCE/Mark Boulton, page 53 below; The Image Bank, pages 135 (G. Covian), 171 above; Images Colour Library, pages 28, 124; Intermediate Technology, page 165; International Rice Research Institute, Philippines, page 163 below; Katz Pictures, pages 12 (Shigeo Kogure/Time Magazine), 14 (Garcia), 157 (David Gordon); Landform Slides, page 48; The Meteorological Office, London Weather Centre, page 79 left; Mikes-Eye, page 161 above; National Meteorological Library, page 73 (G.A. Robinson); Overseas Development Administration, © Crown Copyright, pages 176 below left & below right, 184, 185; PA News, page 36 (John Giles); John Pallister, pages 22, 27, 39, 95 below, 98, 101, 112, 114 centre, 117, 119, 126, 129; Panos Pictures, page 54 (Dylan Garcia), 144 (Jeremey Hartley), 201 (Michael Harvey); O.M. Phillipson, page 215 below, 216; Planet Earth Pictures, pages 29 above (Mark Mattock), 59 (John Lythgoe), 152 below (P.N. Raven), 169 (William M. Smithey), 219 (Jonathan Scott); Popperfoto/Reuter, pages 5,7,15, 213; Rex Features/SIPA-PRESS, page 136; Science Photo Library, pages 71 (European Space Agency), 80 (Noaa), 133 (Brian Brake), 206-7 (Tom Van Sant/Geosphere Project, Santa Monica); Sealand Aerial Photography, pages 37, 81; The Skyscan Photolibrary, pages 67, 122, 137; Still Pictures, pages 55, 87 & 100 (Mark Edwards), 88 left (Alan Watson), 177 (Teit Hornbak), 182 (Mark Edwards), 193 centre (Mark Edwards), 194 (Edward Parker), 195 above (David Brain), 195 below, 199, 200; Tony Stone Images, pages 6 (Alan Kearney), 9 (Paul Chesley), 10 (James Balog), 21 (Ian Murphy), 34 (Herb Schmitz), 41 (Shaun Egan), 53 above (Paul Harris), 77 below (Hugh Sitton), 88 right (Gary Braasch), 111 (Mark Segal), 157 (Simon Jauncey), 155 (Trevor Wood), 161 below (Penny Tweedie), 165 (Penny Tweedie), 189 (Arnulf Husmo), 191 (Joseph Pobereskin), 192 below (Wayne Eastep), 195 centre (Chris Kapolka), 209, 212 (Jeremy Walker); Sygma, pages 176 above (Raymond Reuter), 205 (Philippe Eranian); Telegraph Colour Library, page 139 above (Charles Briscoe-Knight); Topham Picturepoint, pages 11 (Associated Press), 159 above (Associated Press), 211 (Press Association); Tropix, pages 76 (P. Henley), 141 (Ian Spark); University of Dundee, page 79 right; Viewfinder/Bob Thwaites, page 182; Tony Waltham, pages 62, 63 below; The Yorkshire Dales National Park Committee, page 156; Zefa, pages 30 below (K. Kerth), 163 above (M. Prabhu).

Front cover and title page: satellite view of coastal bay and tributaries, Madagascar. Telegraph Colour Library.

We have been unable to trace the copyright holder of the cartoon on page 187 and we would be grateful for any information that would enable us to trace them.

Tectonic activity

A survivor wanders through the destroyed streets of Kobe, Japan

Plate tectonics

The earth's crust

The crust of the earth is made up of a number of **tectonic plates** (Source 1). These plates move over the surface of the globe. When two plates are moving apart, for example in the oceans, the margin between them is called a **constructive plate margin**. It is called this because new crust is being created along the mid-ocean ridge in the Atlantic Ocean. When two plates move towards each other, like the Nazca plate and the South American plate, the margin between them is called a **destructive plate margin**.

Source 1	The world's tectonic plates

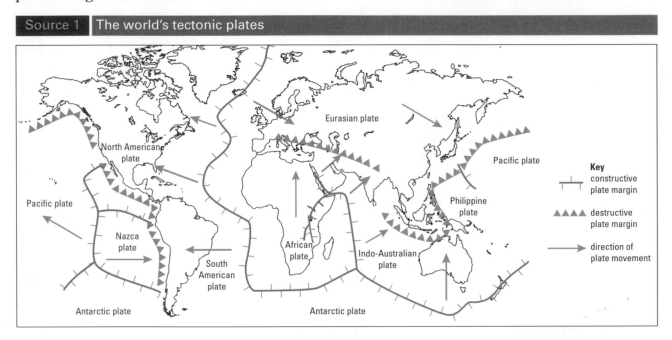

Along the plate margins powerful forces are at work. These forces:

- push up whole landscapes into high mountains by bending or folding the rocks, for example – the Cascade mountains in North America (Source 2) have been crumpled up as the North American plate crashes into the Pacific plate
- cause destruction by **earthquakes**, like the huge tremor which hit the Japanese city of Kobe in 1995 (see Unit 1.4)
- lead to the eruption of volcanoes such as Mount Rainer (Source 2) in the USA and Mount Ruapehu in New Zealand (Source 3).

Source 2	The constructive power of tectonic forces

The volcanic peak of Mount Rainier rises above the folded Cascade mountains in north-west USA where the North American and Pacific plates meet.

Forces beneath the crust

It is hot beneath the surface of the earth. The heat is so great that the rocks below the crust are molten. This molten rock is called **magma**.

At particular places, called 'hot spots', magma rises to the surface in a series of **convection currents.** When the currents reach just below the crust they can rise no more. Instead, the hot currents spread out and carry the crust in a series of plates across the globe, as shown in Source 4.

As the convection currents spread out they pull the crust apart (A in Source 4). At this point a crack in the crust is formed called a **rift valley.** Molten magma reaches the surface through this crack, producing volcanoes and, under the ocean, **ocean ridges**. Here, new crust is being constructed, hence the name 'constructive plate margin'.

Convection currents also move the crust towards other plates. One of the plates will be forced down beneath the other at the **subduction zone** (B in Source 4). The rocks left on the other plate are crumpled into high **fold mountains**. The crust which has been dragged beneath the surface is destroyed – hence these margins are called 'destructive plate margins'. In fact some of the lost crust is heated up to form new magma which eventually finds its way back to the earth's surface.

| Source 3 | The destructive power of tectonic forces |

Wherever the tectonic plates are being pulled apart or crushed together, earthquakes can occur. Shock waves travel through the rocks causing violent movements of the land which destroy settlements and may also lead to loss of life.

Sometimes the plates pass alongside each other, neither colliding nor pulling apart. These plate margins are known as **conservative plate margins,** since crustal material is neither being created nor lost.

| Source 4 | Forces beneath the crust |

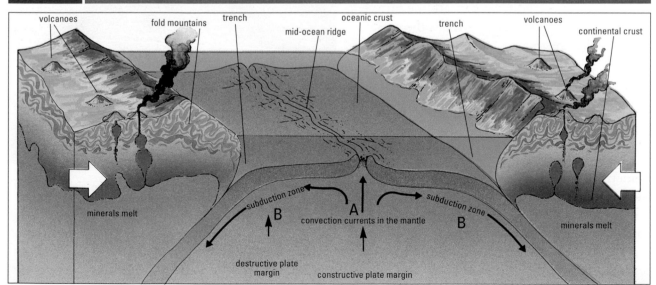

Volcanic activity

Volcanic activity is important right across the earth's surface. There are over 500 active volcanoes which still erupt from time to time. Each year there are around 30 or 40 eruptions. Some eruptions are slight, but others have serious effects, causing loss of life and damage to land and property.

Volcanic activity can be divided into two types (Source 1):

- **intrusive volcanic activity** – where **lava** (molten rock) cools and solidifies beneath the surface
- **extrusive volcanic activity** – where lava reaches the earth's surface before it cools and solidifies.

Source 1	Intrusive and extrusive volcanic landforms

Intrusive

Extrusive

Key
- lava/magma
- ash
- surrounding (country) rock

dykes   batholith   sill

ash and cinder volcano

lava volcano

lava plateau

Intrusive volcanic activity

Volcanoes are an obvious sign of volcanic activity. However, a whole range of landforms result from volcanic activity (Source 1). On the left of the diagram there are examples of landforms which have been produced by molten rock cooling and solidifying beneath the surface. When it is under the earth's surface the molten rock is called **magma.**

When a large amount of liquid rock pushes up towards the earth's surface it will cause all the surface rock to bulge up into a dome or plateau. Such a large mass of solidified magma is known as a **batholith.**

Sometimes smaller veins of magma push out of the batholith and reach the surface elsewhere. Some are called **dykes,** which will stand up above the surrounding land if they resist erosion more than the surrounding rocks; if they are less resistant they form ditches. Others are called **sills.** They reach the surface by forcing their way

Source 2	Upstanding dyke in northern Scotland

surrounding (country) rock

upstanding dyke

between layers of rock. They produce steep-sided ledges on the surface.

Source 2 is a dyke on the island of Skye in northern Scotland. It is more resistant to erosion than the surrounding rock. It stands up like a 'wall' running across the land.

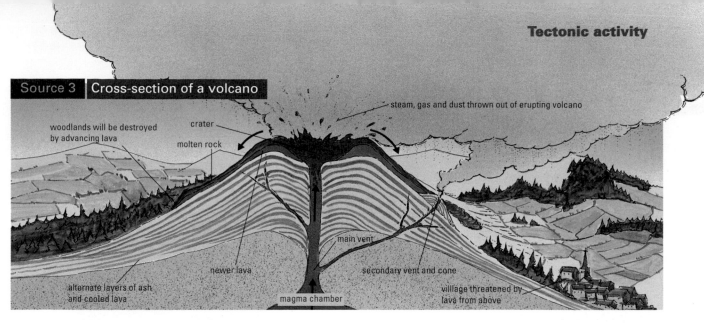

| Source 3 | Cross-section of a volcano |

steam, gas and dust thrown out of erupting volcano

woodlands will be destroyed by advancing lava

crater

molten rock

main vent

newer lava

secondary vent and cone

alternate layers of ash and cooled lava

magma chamber

village threatened by lava from above

Extrusive volcanic activity

Extrusive volcanic landforms are shown on the right-hand side of Source 1. The best known of these is the volcano. This is essentially a crack in the earth's surface which provides an outlet for lava, steam and **ash**. The lava passes through a pipe called the **vent** on its way from inside the crust to the earth's surface, during a volcanic eruption (Source 3). After an eruption a **crater** is left at the top of the vent. The lava from the volcano cools on the earth's surface.

The escape of lava from a volcano often takes place under pressure, and results in volcanic explosions with steam, gas and dust being hurled high into the air and molten rock pouring down the sides of the volcano (Source 4).

Volcanoes take many different forms (Source 5). Eruptions may damage property – houses, roads and farmland. Equally serious are the possible long-term effects of volcanic eruptions. The dust which reaches the upper layers of the atmosphere can partly block out the sun's heat and may lead to higher levels of rainfall.

Volcanoes can also have positive effects. Volcanic ash and lava turn into fertile soil, and hot magma beneath the surface can provide a source of steam energy when it heats up underground water.

| Source 4 | Volcano erupting on Big Island, Hawaii |

| Source 5 | Types of volcano |

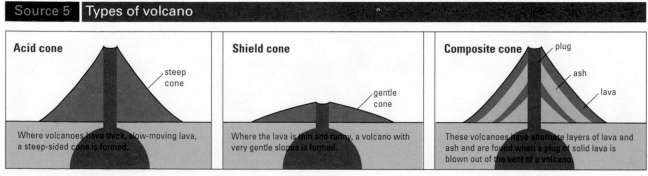

Acid cone

steep cone

Where volcanoes have thick, slow-moving lava, a steep-sided cone is formed.

Shield cone

gentle cone

Where the lava is thin and runny, a volcano with very gentle slopes is formed.

Composite cone

plug

ash

lava

These volcanoes have alternate layers of lava and ash and are found when a plug of solid lava is blown out of the vent of a volcano.

Faults and earthquakes

Faults

Tectonic plates may move towards each other, away from each other or slide against each other. When they do move they make the earth's crust crack. These cracks are called **faults**.

Source 1 shows two types of fault. One is known as a **lateral fault**. This is when the crust at A is sliding along the crust at B. This is what is happening along the San Andreas fault in California, USA (Source 2). The other kind of fault shown in Source 1 is the **vertical fault**. Here, the crust at B has slipped down away from the crust at C.

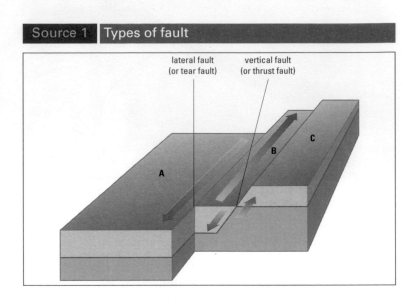

| Source 1 | Types of fault |

When there is movement along these fault lines, the jagged rocks catch against each other. Each movement may only be a millimetre at any one time. However, over the years the pressure on the 'caught' rock will build up and become extreme. Eventually the rocks will spring apart. When they do so, earthquakes happen.

Earthquakes

Every year, several thousand earth movements are detected around the world. Usually only 40 or 50 of these are violent enough to cause serious damage. However, when they do occur, earthquakes like the one near the village of Killari in India (Source 3) can result in loss of life.

| Source 2 | The San Andreas fault runs down the western side of California |

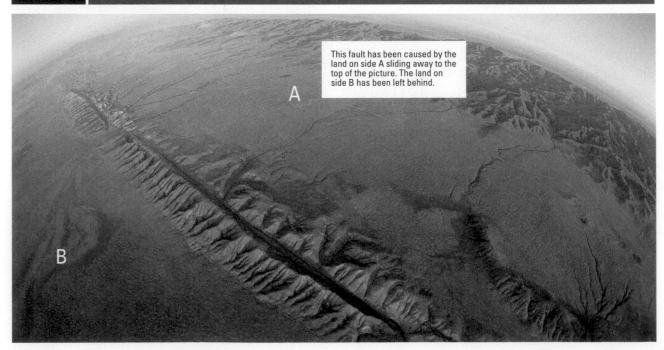

This fault has been caused by the land on side A sliding away to the top of the picture. The land on side B has been left behind.

Disaster at Killari

At 4 o'clock in the morning on 30 September 1993, the village of Killari in central India was destroyed by a severe earthquake. Killari is 450 km east of Bombay. Several of the villages around Killari were destroyed, 30 000 people lost their lives and many more were left homeless. The quake measured 6.4 on the Richter Scale.

When earthquakes occur, the point underground where rocks spring apart is known as the **focus**. From the focus (Source 4), shock waves travel through the rocks in all directions. As the shock waves reach the surface they will damage houses, factories and roads.

Most damage will be caused on the earth's surface closest to the focus. This point, directly above the focus, is called the **epicentre**. By the time the shock waves have reached the surface further away, they have lost most of their energy and less damage is caused.

How far the damage extends depends, also, on the nature of the rocks. Hard, resistant rocks will quickly reduce the energy of the shock waves.

Softer rocks will buckle and bend, and the shock waves will be able to carry their destructive power to places further away.

Earthquakes in less economically developed countries (LEDCs) are much more damaging than those in more economically developed countries (MEDCs). Often the buildings cannot resist the shock waves – as they have been poorly built. They are often made of heavy, local rock. When the buildings collapse the people inside have little chance. Few LEDCs are able to mount a quick rescue operation – their emergency services are usually few in number and not well trained. Many people died in Killari (Source 3), because the Indian government did not have the resources to respond quickly enough.

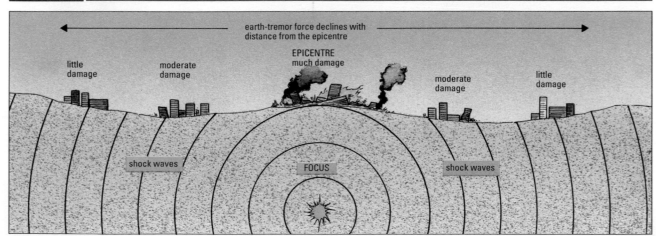

Tectonic hazards
the Kobe earthquake, 1995

Early in the morning on Tuesday 17 January 1995 the shock waves of a huge earthquake roared through the city of Kobe, near the ancient Japanese capital of Kyoto. Measuring 7.2 on the Richter Scale, it was the worst earthquake to hit Japan for 50 years.

- More than 3500 people were killed.
- Some 20 000 houses were destroyed.
- About 250 000 people were left homeless.
- Operations at Japan's largest port (Kobe) ceased.
- An area of over 100 hectares was completely destroyed by fire.
- The cost of the damage is estimated at over US$50 billion.

This earthquake was caused by the Philippine plate moving beneath the Eurasian plate (Source 1). The rocks had locked together many years ago, and the pressure had built up each year since then. Suddenly they jerked free, and the shock waves were released. The destruction is shown in the photograph on page 5, in Sources 1 and 2, and is also described in the newspaper article in Source 3.

The epicentre of the earthquake was near Awaji Island. Here only buildings were destroyed. The greatest destruction was where most people live – in the cities of Kobe, Akashi and Ashiya. The famous bullet train tracks, motorways and bridges were all badly damaged. Broken gas pipes and electricity lines caused fires to rage throughout the built-up areas – especially among the many wooden houses built to withstand the shock waves.

| Source 1 | Damage from the Kobe quake |

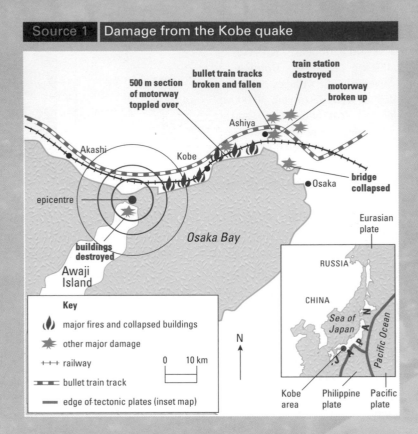

| Source 2 | The Kobe earthquake |

Source 3 | Newspaper report of earthquake damage

Kobe – the quake's aftermath

An empty noodle shop, in Kobe's central shopping and entertainment district, suddenly caught fire yesterday. The blaze, one of many hampering earthquake relief efforts, quickly consumed 10 surrounding buildings.

Police and Japan's military forces, later tried to clear some of the damage in the district, where the walls of Daimaru, a department store, fell on the main road.

Most of the initial fires ignited by Tuesday's quake have been damped. Yesterday, firefighters were trying to kill the last of the flames. Shop signs, melted and mangled from the heat, were strewn about and dust and smoke filled the air.

Construction workers tried to overhaul parts of the elevated Hanshin Expressway collapsed on to the main road between Osaka and Kobe. The damage has blocked part of the road, forcing traffic to follow other routes and causing severe jams.

Although trucks, cranes, power shovels and workmen gathered, nobody seemed to know what to do with the giant concrete structure on it's side, and the massive uprooted pillars, their steel foundations exposed.

And while emergency supplies arrived by trucks from throughout the country, many people blamed the government for its slow reaction. "What are we paying taxes for?" asked a woman. "Isn't it for times like this?"

Source 4 | Building to survive earthquakes

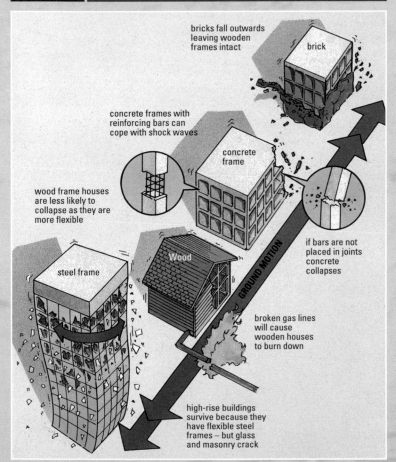

bricks fall outwards leaving wooden frames intact

brick

concrete frames with reinforcing bars can cope with shock waves

concrete frame

wood frame houses are less likely to collapse as they are more flexible

if bars are not placed in joints concrete collapses

Wood

steel frame

GROUND MOTION

broken gas lines will cause wooden houses to burn down

high-rise buildings survive because they have flexible steel frames – but glass and masonry crack

Resisting earthquakes

If scientists were able to predict when earthquakes are likely to happen, many lives would be saved. So far this has not been possible. Even if earthquakes could be predicted accurately, they would still damage buildings. Recent earthquakes in different parts of the world have allowed town planners to form a picture of what kinds of buildings can resist earthquakes.

Source 4 shows how different building materials respond to shock waves.

• Wooden houses may burn in the aftermath of an earthquake, as they did in Kobe.

• Bricks fall out of buildings, so they are not good materials in earthquake zones.

• Concrete is much better, as long as it is reinforced by strong, flexible steel bars.

• High-rise buildings with flexible steel frames do survive, but falling glass and bricks can cause injury and death.

These are the lessons which the people of Kobe must pay attention to as they rebuild their city.

Tectonic hazards
the eruption of Mount Pinatubo

Mount Pinatubo is a volcanic mountain located about 100 km north-west of Manila, the capital of the Philippines (Source 1). By June 1991, the volcano had been peaceful for more than six centuries. During this time the ash and lava from previous eruptions had weathered to become fertile soil which was used to cultivate rice. Then, suddenly, the volcano came to life (Source 2).

Advance warning that the volcano was about to erupt gave the authorities time to evacuate thousands of people from the nearby town of Angeles. Some 15 000 American airmen and women also left the nearby Clark air base. The level of activity increased and finally on 12 June the volcano sent a cloud of steam and ash some 30 km up into the atmosphere. What happened next can be seen in the Fact File on page 15.

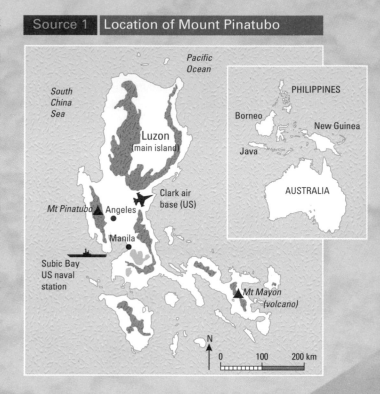

Source 1 | **Location of Mount Pinatubo**

Source 2 | **Pinatubo erupts in June 1991**

Fact File | **The Pinatubo eruption**

Boiling mud swamps towns

Philippines. Hundreds of Filipinos were plucked from the roofs of their houses yesterday after walls of boiling mud swamped towns. Torrential rain from Tropical Storm Nina loosened a torrent of volcanic debris, called lahar, from Pinatubo volcano which swept into towns. More than 65 000 people were forced to flee the area.

A spokesperson for the regional disaster office said: 'We had already been hit by a 10 ft lahar last week. And then Bacolor got hit with another 10 feet of lahar today.'

Bacolor, a town of 20 000 people, was turned into a wasteland of mud and ash. Houses were buried, forcing residents to haul their beds, cooking pots and clothes to the roof.

Helicopters evacuated scores, but many refused to go, not wanting to leave their belongings behind.

- Ash fell to a depth of 50 cm near the volcano, and over a 600 km radius of the volcano it was still over 10 cm deep.
- The volume of ash in the atmosphere turned day to night and hampered the rescue operations.
- Torrential rain accompanied the eruption, and much of the ash was rained back to earth as mud, causing thousands of buildings to collapse under its weight.
- Power supplies were cut and roads and bridges were left unusable, as was the water supply which was quickly contaminated.
- Some 350 people were killed.

The long-term effects

The effects of the eruption were felt long after the volcano became dormant again. With thousands of people living in refugee camps, malaria and diarrhoea quickly spread. Huge quantities of dust, some 20 million tonnes, were left in the atmosphere. Scientists believe that the dust has resulted in a lowering of average temperatures, and that it will delay global warming. Heavy rains following typhoons in the area in 1993 and 1995 (Source 4) caused flooding. This swept layers of ash and dust from the steep slopes of the volcano down on to lower land in the form of avalanches of mud, or **lahars.**

Source 3 | **Filipinos flee the lahar, 5 September 1995**

Volcanic areas
Iceland and southern Italy

Volcanoes are usually destructive. Eruptions often lead to loss of life and may also damage property and crops. However, volcanic activity can also have positive results.

Iceland

Iceland is situated in the North Atlantic Ocean. It is also located on a major plate boundary – the mid-Atlantic ridge (Source 1) As a result of this, there is a lot of volcanic activity on the island.

- It has over 200 volcanoes.
- There are over 800 hot springs and geysers (Source 2).
- Ten per cent of the land surface is lava fields.
- New land is being created as the two plates (the Eurasian and North American plate) separate along the ridge.

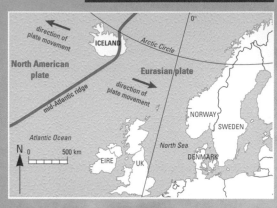

Source 1 | **Iceland on the mid-Atlantic ridge**

Source 2 | **The Strokkur Geyser**

Volcanic activity has some positive effects:

1 **Hot spring water** is carried by pipeline to Reykjavik, the capital of Iceland, giving most people a cheap and reliable form of energy which does not damage the environment. Much of the water used in the city today comes from a borehole 45 km away, which yields water at over 300°C (Source 3).

2 **Electricity is generated** from the geothermal resources of hot water which lie under the ground in many parts of Iceland. Steam from the hot water deposits found underground is used to power turbines, which in turn generate electricity for factories and homes.

3 **Greenhouses** not far from Reykjavik are geothermally heated, allowing some Icelanders to produce vegetables, fruit and even flowers.

Source 3 | **The water in the Laugardalur open-air pool in Reykjavik is naturally hot**

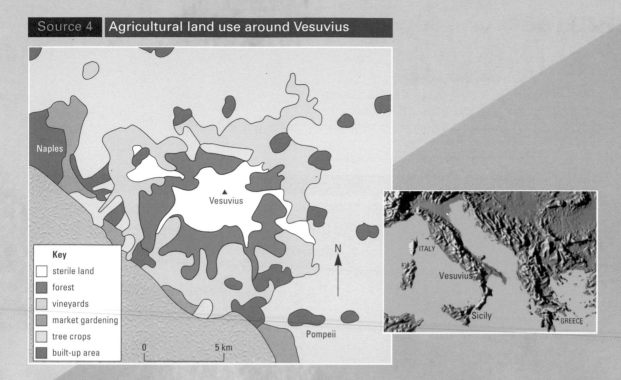

Key
- sterile land
- forest
- vineyards
- market gardening
- tree crops
- built-up area

0   5 km

Naples

Vesuvius

Pompeii

N

ITALY

Vesuvius

Sicily

GREECE

Southern Italy

In southern Italy, volcanic activity has brought different benefits. Just over 1900 years ago, in AD 79, the volcano Vesuvius erupted. The town of Pompeii was completely destroyed. The eruption sent burning gases down the sides of the volcano killing the people of the town. Ash from this eruption, together with many smaller ones that have taken place since, has covered the landscape in this part of southern Italy.

Over many years, the ash has weathered to produce fertile soils. This has led to many people settling around the volcano, where the soils are used to grow olives, fruit, vines and nuts as well as a variety of market garden produce (Sources 4 and 5). Villages and towns circle the higher, sterile slopes, where the lava has not yet weathered, so nothing can be grown. In other places where the ash and lava are loose, forests have been planted to stop slope erosion.

The slopes of Vesuvius, in spite of the ever-present danger of new volcanic eruptions, will always provide rich soils to encourage farmers to work the land.

Source 5   The fertile land around Vesuvius

1 Make a copy of the volcano (Source 1).
   a Label the following features:
      magma chamber; main vent; crater; steam, gas and dust;
      layers of cooled lava.
   b Explain how and why a volcano erupts.

Source 1	Volcano

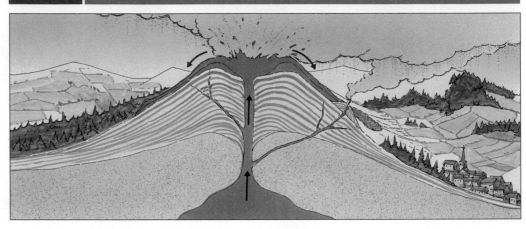

2 a On an outline map of the world, mark in and label the following features:
      i   the main tectonic plates
      ii the constructive plate margins
      iii the destructive plate margins.
   b Briefly describe what happens to the earth's crust at:
      i   a constructive plate margin
      ii a destructive plate margin.

3 Copy the diagram in Source 2 and add these labels in the correct places:
   mantle, oceanic crust, volcano, continental crust, convection current.

Source 2	Tectonic landforms and processes

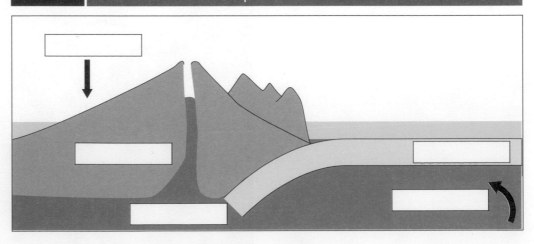

4 a Explain the terms intrusive and extrusive.
  b What do the following terms mean?
    i magma
    ii lava
  c Why do some volcanoes have steep sides but others have more gentle slopes?

5 a Draw a simple diagram showing the difference between a lateral fault and a vertical fault. Name a specific example of one type of fault you have studied.
  b Describe what happens at the focus of an earthquake.
  c At which point on the earth's surface are the shock waves of an earthquake felt most strongly?

6 Study Source 3.
  a Recent eruptions have left five different marks on the landscape. Describe each mark of volcanic activity.
  b i In the last eruption which side of the mountain erupted?
    ii When the eruption took place, from which direction was the wind blowing?
  c Why are there so many villages located on the land covered by volcanic ash?
  d Why are there no villages lying to the east of the volcano?
  e The River South is the only river with villages along it – why?
  f Port Haven is likely to be quite safe from volcanic dangers – why?
  g Draw a simple sketch of the map. Mark on it suitably safe, but short, routes for roads linking Port Haven with all the villages shown on the map.

Source 3	Mount Pluto and the surrounding area

Key
- mud flows at times of eruption
- lahar
- lava
- ---- limits of recent blast area
- ····· limits of recent ash deposits
- ● villages
- — coastline
- steep mountain slopes
- crater

1 Plate tectonics

Tectonic plates are carried across the earth's surface on convection currents of liquid magma. Where these plates pull apart from each other the growing spaces between them are known as constructive plate margins. Where these plates crash into each other the crash zones are known as destructive plate margins. Some plates slide along each other, without pulling apart or colliding. These are known as conservative plate margins.

2 Volcanic activity

There are two kinds of volcanic activity: intrusive and extrusive. Intrusive rock is magma hardening beneath the surface. Intrusive landforms are dykes, sills and batholiths. Extrusive rock is when the liquid magma flows out on to the land surface as lava. Extrusive landforms include volcanic cones and lava plateaus.

The types of volcano are:
• acid cone volcano – steep sided cone is formed
• shield cone volcano – volcano with gentle slopes is formed
• composite cone volcano – made up of alternate layers of lava and ash.

Volcanic ash and lava weathers into deep, fertile soil. In many parts of the world people live and farm on volcanic slopes in spite of the dangers. In southern Italy the slopes of Vesuvius are intensively farmed in spite of the volcano's destructive history.

3 Faults and earthquakes

Faults are cracks in the earth's surface. When rocks slide horizontally along the crack it is called a lateral fault. When they slide vertically along the crack it is a vertical fault. As the rocks slide against each other they 'snag'. If they jerk free an earthquake occurs.

The point from which shock waves come is called the focus of the earthquake. When the shock waves reach the surface they cause great damage. Most damage is on the earth's surface directly above the focus – a point called the epicentre.

4 Tectonic hazards: the Kobe earthquake

In 1995 the Japanese city of Kobe was badly damaged by a violent earthquake. Over 3500 people were killed. Buildings toppled and wooden houses were burnt by fires caused by escaping gas and exposed electricity lines. Communications were also disrupted.

5 Tectonic hazards: the eruption of Mount Pinatubo

Erupting volcanoes pour hot lava and burning gases down their slopes, destroying everything in their path. Later, after heavy rain, mudslides of loose ash and cinder, called lahar, may pour down on to the towns and villages around. This happened on the slopes of Mount Pinatubo in the Philippines in 1995.

6 Volcanic areas: Iceland and southern Italy

Beneath volcanoes there is a reservoir of liquid magma. This heats up the water in the rock. The hot water can be piped to nearby towns and villages. Steam from the water is used to generate electricity. In Iceland, volcanic activity provides hot water for domestic use, electricity and other benefits.

Rivers and the hydrological cycle

The Victoria Falls on the Zambezi River, Africa

River systems and processes

Fresh water is essential for life on earth. Water that reaches the land surface forms part of the **water cycle**, also called the **hydrological cycle** (Source 1). The main input into the system is **precipitation.** This is usually rain, but in high mountain areas snow is frequent as well. Water may flow quickly through the system as **runoff** on the surface, in the form of rivers transferring water from land to sea. Energy from the sun **evaporates** sea water: it changes liquid water into water vapour in the atmosphere. As the water vapour is drawn higher up into the atmosphere, it is cooled. The water vapour may **condense** into water droplets which can be seen as clouds. Precipitation falls from clouds that are sufficiently tall and thick, and the water cycle begins all over again.

The water cycle is more complicated than this, however. Some of the rain water may never reach the sea; instead it is lost directly back into the atmosphere from the leaves of plants. This process is known as **evapo-transpiration.** Some of the rain water is **intercepted** by trees so that its

flow is delayed. Precipitation that falls as snow can be stored in glaciers on the surface (Source 2). Rainwater may be stored in lakes. Some rain water seeps down through the soil. This is the process of **infiltration.** Some of the infiltrated water seeps further down to fill empty spaces in the rock, which is known as **percolation.** The water can only do this until it reaches the level called the **water table.** Below this level the spaces in the rock have already been filled with water. At this point the water flows sideways as **groundwater flow**, as Source 1 shows.

Source 2 | Perito Moreno glacier

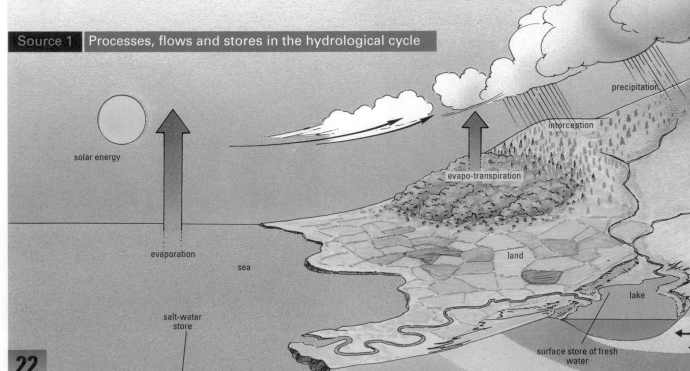

Source 1 | Processes, flows and stores in the hydrological cycle

solar energy

precipitation

interception

evapo-transpiration

evaporation

sea

land

lake

salt-water store

surface store of fresh water

Source 3 | The drainage basin

confluence

mouth

(A)

tributary

source

(B)

Key

(A)(B) drainage basins

••••• watershed

lowland

upland

Source 4 | Factors affecting the rate of runoff

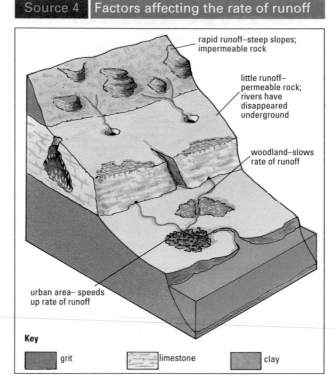

rapid runoff–steep slopes; impermeable rock

little runoff– permeable rock; rivers have disappeared underground

woodland–slows rate of runoff

urban area– speeds up rate of runoff

Key

grit   limestone   clay

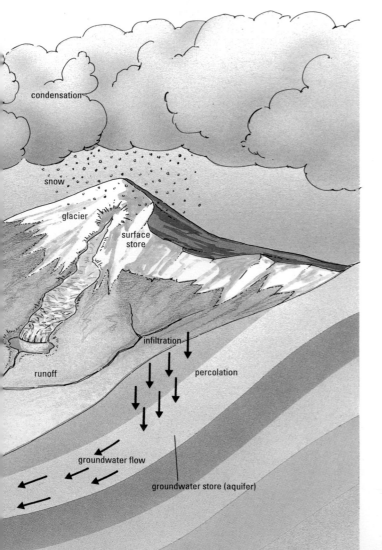

condensation

snow

glacier

surface store

infiltration

percolation

runoff

groundwater flow

groundwater store (aquifer)

Each river has its own **drainage basin.** Each drainage basin has its own inputs, flows, stores and outputs. As Source 3 shows, it is possible to draw a definite dividing line between each drainage basin. It follows the tops of the hills and is called the **watershed.** The main river has its source in the higher parts of the basin where most precipitation falls. Smaller streams or **tributaries** join up with the main river; they meet at a **confluence.** The **mouth** of the river is where it meets the sea.

Each drainage basin has its own features of rock type, relief (shape of the land) and land use and these affect how quickly or how slowly the water moves through the basin. Source 4 shows how the features of a drainage basin can affect runoff. The rock type and relief are physical factors over which humans have little influence. However, land use is different. Land uses can be changed by people. Urban areas increase the rate of runoff. The rain water hits solid surfaces such as roofs, pavements and roads; the water is led into drains which speed up its overland flow into rivers.

The river and its valley in the uplands

The river's course from source to mouth is summarised by its **long profile** (Source 1). The profile is steep and irregular when the river is flowing well above sea level in the uplands, but much gentler and smoother as the river nears the sea.

The main work of any river is to transfer rain water from land to sea. Most of its energy is used simply to keep the water flowing, because it needs to overcome the friction of the river's bed and banks. It may have some spare energy to transport its load of fine material and pebbles. There are four ways in which a river transports its load: solution, suspension, saltation and traction. Source 2 shows how each of these works.

The river is, therefore, an **agent of transport,** carrying material from upland to lowland regions. It is also an **agent of erosion.** There are four ways in which a river undertakes the work of erosion (Source 3).

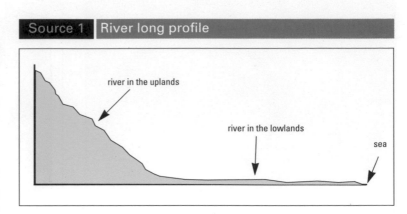

Source 1 River long profile

river in the uplands

river in the lowlands

sea

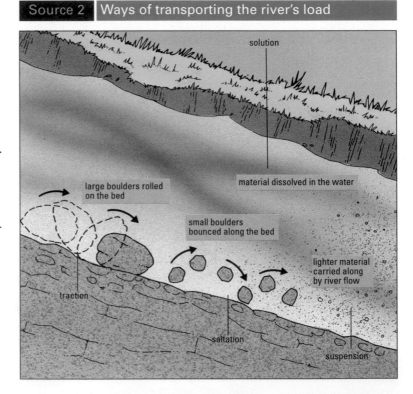

Source 2 Ways of transporting the river's load

solution

material dissolved in the water

large boulders rolled on the bed

small boulders bounced along the bed

lighter material carried along by river flow

traction

saltation

suspension

Source 3 Process of river erosion

Abrasion or corrosion	Hydraulic action
The pebbles being transported remove material from the bed and banks of the river channel, by wearing them away.	The sheer force of the water by itself may be sufficient to dislodge material and erode the bed and sides of the channel.
Solution or corrosion	**Attrition**
Some rocks are subject to chemical attack: chalk and limestone, for example, slowly dissolve in water.	The particles are knocked about as they are being transported. They are reduced in size to sand and eventually to even smaller silt-sized particles. These are more easily moved by the water.

Source 4 shows a river in the uplands. Labels have been added which describe the channel and valley features.

steep sided, V-shaped valley

waterfall

interlocking spurs

River landforms in the uplands

The main landforms found in the uplands – steep **V-shaped valley**, **interlocking spurs**, **waterfall** and **gorge** (Source 5) – have all been formed by the processes of river erosion already referred to.

The steep-sided V-shaped valley is formed by **vertical erosion**. The river is flowing so high above sea level that its main work is cutting downwards, which is what vertical erosion means. By the processes of abrasion and hydraulic action, the river erodes the rocks on its bed making the valley deeper. There is mass movement of material down the sides of the valley because the valley is so steep and deep.

Interlocking spurs are formed where the river swings from side to side. Again the main work of the river is vertical erosion into the rock on its bed by abrasion and hydraulic action. This means that the river cuts down to flow between spurs of higher land on alternate sides of the valley.

Waterfalls occur where a hard band of rock outcrops which is much more resistant to erosion than the softer rock below it. The river can only slowly erode the hard band of rock; it can erode more quickly the soft rock below. The soft rock is eroded also by the force of the water as it falls, which creates a **plunge pool** at the bottom of the falls. The waterfall gradually retreats upstream leaving a gorge below it. The gorge is protected from erosion by its capping of hard rock.

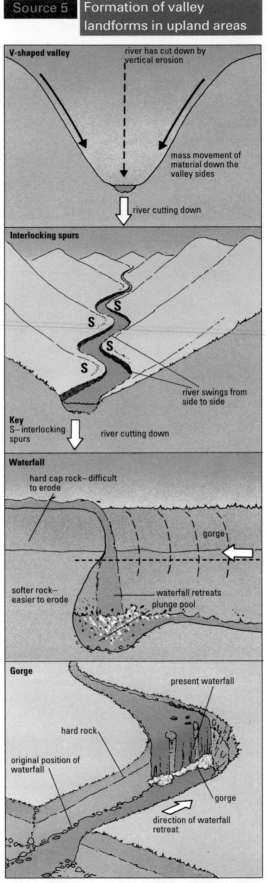

Source 5 | Formation of valley landforms in upland areas

V-shaped valley
river has cut down by vertical erosion
mass movement of material down the valley sides
river cutting down

Interlocking spurs
S S S S
river swings from side to side
Key
S – interlocking spurs
river cutting down

Waterfall
hard cap rock – difficult to erode
gorge
softer rock – easier to erode
waterfall retreats
plunge pool

Gorge
present waterfall
hard rock
original position of waterfall
gorge
direction of waterfall retreat

The river and its valley in the lowlands

The river and valley features (Source 1) change as lowland regions are reached: the river channel is wider and deeper; there are fewer large stones in the bed and river flow can be as fast as in the uplands despite the more gentle gradient; the plan of the river is less straight because of the many meanders; the river can often split up into **distributaries** near the sea to form a **delta**; the valley cross-section is wider and flatter, and includes the **floodplain** where the distinctive landforms include **levées** and **ox-bow lakes**.

River and valley features

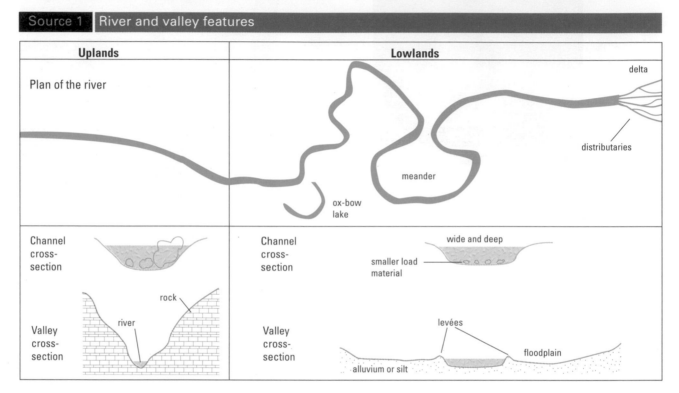

The river is still an agent of erosion, but vertical erosion is less important because the river is too close to sea level. More important is **lateral erosion** where the river wears away the sides of the channel, especially on the outside of bends.

The river becomes an agent of **deposition** as well. Such a large load of material has been picked up that, once the river loses energy, it drops some of the material it is transporting. Energy is lost when the river flow gets slower, such as on the inside of a bend or where the river meets the sea.

The greatest thickness of river-deposited material, called **alluvium**, is on the floodplain. As its names suggests, the floodplain is an area of flat

Source 2 | Formation of the floodplain and levées

land formed by flooding. Every time the river leaves its channel, it is slowed down and begins to deposit **silt** across the valley floor. A great thickness of alluvial material builds up. The largest amount of deposition is always on the banks of the channel, which builds up to a greater height than the rest of the floodplain to form levées (Source 2).

Meanders and ox-bow lakes

A study of the formation of meanders and ox-bow lakes shows how the river both deposits and erodes laterally (Source 3).

The force of the water undercuts the bank on the outside of a bend to form a steep bank to the channel, called a **river cliff**. An underwater current with a spiral flow carries the eroded material to the inside of the bend where the flow of water is slow. Here the material is deposited to form a gentle bank, called a **slip-off slope**.

The bend of the meander becomes even more pronounced as lateral erosion continues (Source 4). Especially in times of flood, when the river's energy is much greater, the narrow neck of the meander may be broken so that the river flows straight again. This forms an ox-bow lake by cutting off the old meander loop. Deposition during the flooding may seal off the edges of the lake. The lateral erosion on the outside bank of the meander helps to widen the floodplain.

Source 3	Formation of meanders and ox-bow lakes

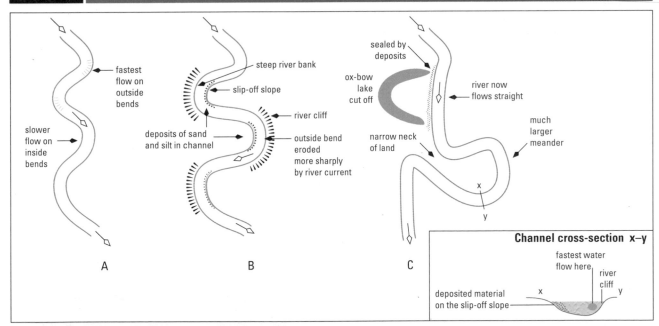

Source 4	A meandering river

Most British rivers are relatively small and go out to sea through estuaries. There are often one or two deep water channels between extensive deposits of sand and mud. An example is the River Tay on pages 32–3. Bigger rivers in other parts of the world may split up just before reaching the sea and form a delta. The River Ganges, which is described on pages 34–5, does this.

Causes of river floods

After a rainstorm, there is an increase in the river's **discharge** (the amount of water flowing in the river). This can be shown on a storm hydrograph (Source 1).

Most rainstorms will do no more than fill up the river channel, as shown for point B in Source 1. Flooding only occurs when the river channel has reached bankfull level and more water is still reaching the channel. The river reaches bursting point at C and floods the surrounding land at D (Source 2). Weather conditions which favour the greatest amount of runoff in the river's drainage basin are the main cause of flooding. Imagine that the rainstorm shown in Source 1 gave more rain and lasted longer. A point will be reached when the river discharge will be too great for the channel (Source 2). This is happening to the river in Source 3.

Three weather conditions are likely to cause extensive flooding.

1 **Large amounts of rain day after day** – rain saturates the ground so no more rain can infiltrate or percolate into the ground.

2 **A cloudburst in a thunderstorm** – the rain droplets are so large and hit the ground so fast that there is little chance of any seepage into the ground.

3 **Melting snow and ice** – a sudden increase in temperature can begin a rapid thaw to the point where the river cannot cope with the increased amount of water.

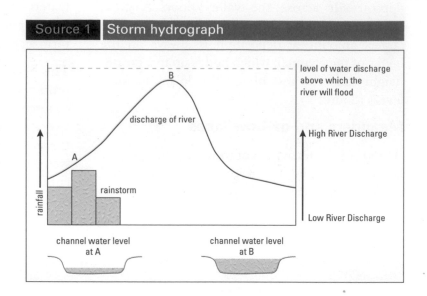

Source 1 | Storm hydrograph

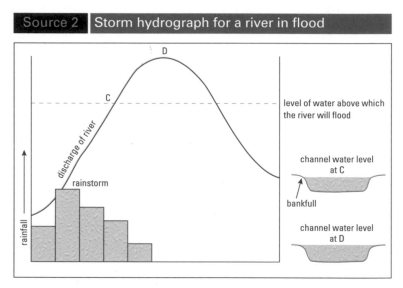

Source 2 | Storm hydrograph for a river in flood

Source 3 | A river in flood

Source 4 | Immediate effects of river floods

Effects of river flooding

Flooding greatly increases a river's energy so that it can do more work. In times of flood, the deeper and faster river increases its load dramatically. Most rivers turn brown when in flood because of the large amount of material they are carrying in suspension. The amount of erosion by hydraulic action and abrasion is greatly increased. Many of the valley landforms in lowland areas have been formed by flooding. Levées and floodplains are formed by deposition after the river overflows its banks. Ox-bow lakes are cut off when the force of the river enables it to break through the meander neck.

River floods can cause a lot of damage. As with all the natural hazards, there are both immediate and long-term effects. The immediate effects of a river flood include loss of life, destruction of property and crops, and the disruption of communications (Source 4). The consequences can be serious. Many lives have been lost in floods along the big rivers in China – the Huang Ho is called 'China's sorrow' because its devastating floods have killed thousands of people. During the Rhine floods in early 1995, people in some Dutch villages had to be evacuated and the river current was too strong for barges to use the river safely.

In the longer term there is the cost of replacing what has been lost and damaged. In rich countries the risks may be covered by insurance. The poor in the less economically developed countries, however, may lose everything. With crop land ruined and animals lost, widespread famine can result. The need for emergency food aid in these circumstances becomes urgent.

People, rivers and floods

Responses to floods

Flood protection measures are in operation along most big rivers. Where the costs of damage from flooding could be enormous, the scheme may be big and expensive such as the Thames Barrier which protects the city of London (Source 1).

Along most rivers the aim is to alter the channel or banks so that the river can carry more water without flooding. The most common measure of flood protection is to increase the height of the natural levées along the banks. This makes the channel deeper so that it can hold more water. Another measure that is often taken is to clean out the channel by dredging to make the river flow more efficiently.

On a much larger scale is the building of dams. In times of great runoff dams hold back water, and the river discharge in the area below the dam can be controlled. Dams can be a very effective measure of flood control but they are an expensive solution. They are often built as part of a scheme of **river basin management**. Not only is there flood control, but the water stored behind the dam can be used to supply houses and factories, irrigate crops and for recreation and shipping, as well as for HEP (hydro-

Source 1 | The Thames Barrier

electric power). This is called a **multi-purpose scheme**. The River Rhône in France is an example of a managed river (Source 2).

Often, however, prevention is better than cure. By cutting down trees and by ploughing up and down slopes people have increased the rate of runoff in some areas, such as on the sides of the Himalayas in Nepal. The frequency and scale of flooding have been increased as a result. More care and attention given to the way in which the land in a drainage basin is used would reduce the risks of floods occurring in the first place.

Source 2 | River Rhône: river basin management

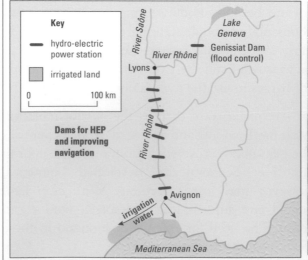

Key

— hydro-electric power station

▇ irrigated land

0   100 km

River Saône

Lake Geneva

Genissiat Dam (flood control)

River Rhône

Lyons

Dams for HEP and improving navigation

River Rhône

Avignon

irrigation water

Mediterranean Sea

hydro-electric power station

river banks strengthened against flooding

canal for boats to use

Human activities in river valleys

One of the reasons why the hazard of river floods affects so many people in so many different countries is because rivers attract people to their sides. Some of the many uses of rivers are illustrated in Source 3.

River valleys offer attractive locations for settlements. It is easier to build on the more gently sloping land. The valley floor is sheltered and warmer than the slopes above. The variety of land uses and the amount of settlement tend to increase as you move from the uplands to the lowlands.

In the uplands, opportunities for farming are restricted by the narrow valley floor, steep slopes and poor climate. It is colder, more cloudy, wetter and windier than on the lowlands. Often only sheep will survive, with cattle grazing the better grasses on the valley floors. There may be good sites for building dams and storing water or even generating hydro-electric power. The flat land on the floodplain, underlain by a great thickness of silt, offers a much better environment for farming. Towns and industries often grow up on the sides of the estuary where the water is deep enough to be navigated by ships. Unfortunately, so many farms, industries and towns next to rivers can create problems of pollution.

Source 3   Land uses in a British river valley

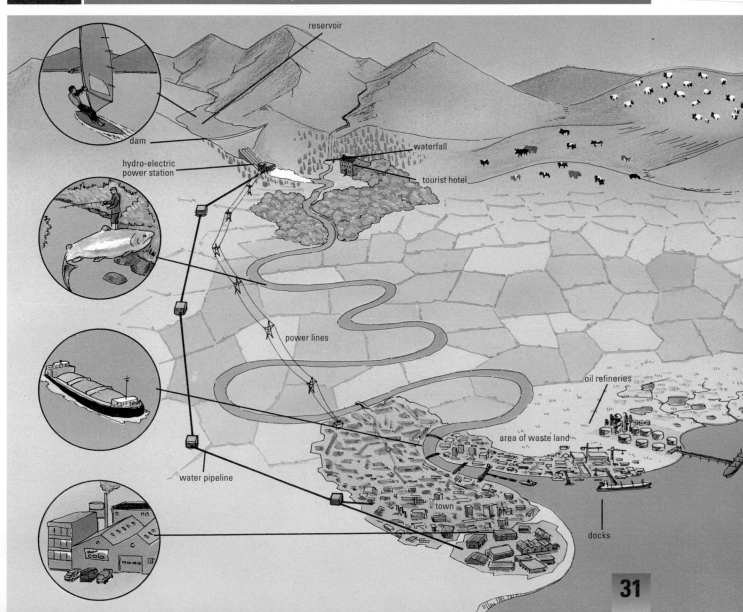

A river and its valley
the River Tay

In the uplands

The River Tay is fed by streams which drain the slopes of the Grampian mountains in the Highlands of Scotland. Precipitation in the upland parts of the drainage basin is high (well over 1000 mm per year) and slopes are steep, which give high amounts of runoff. It is already a big river, about 100 metres across in that part of its course shown on the Ordnance Survey map extract (Source 1).

The valley cross-section is shown in Source 2a. It is V-shaped and steep sided. The river fills the valley floor. The cross-section shows that the river is still flowing at some height above sea level; it is cutting down into the valley floor by vertical erosion.

As for the land uses shown on the map (Source 1), the small settlements and roads are concentrated on the less steep and more sheltered land in the Tay valley.

To the north of the river much of the land is likely to be used for nothing better than rough grazing for sheep and deer. South of the river coniferous (evergreen) woodland is the land use which covers the largest area.

Source 1 | **Part of the upland course of the River Tay**

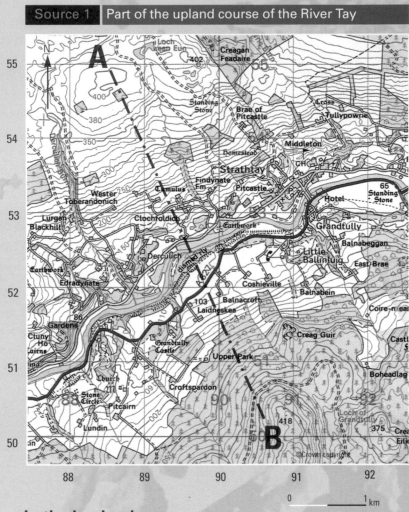

In the lowlands

Source 2b is the valley cross-section near the sea. The flat and low-lying land is the floodplain. It is 0.6 km wide where the tributary River Earn meets the main River Tay.

Source 2 | **Cross-sections across the Tay valley**

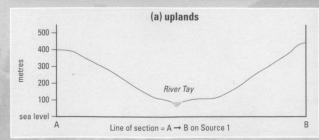

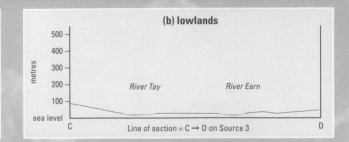

Source 3 | **Part of the floodplain and estuary of the River Tay**

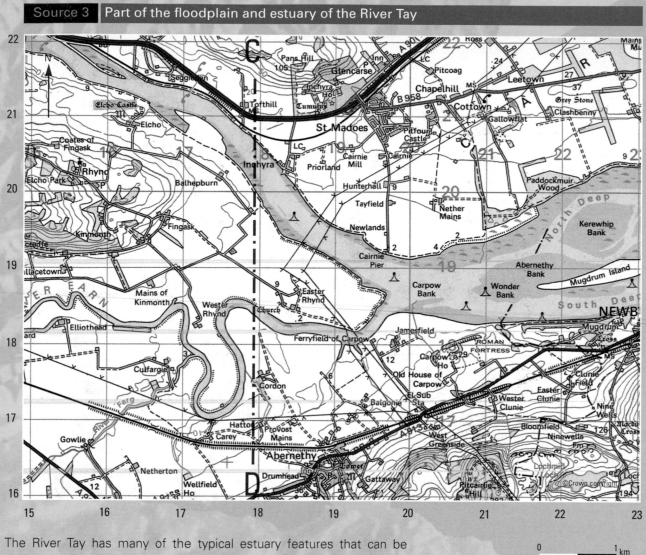

The River Tay has many of the typical estuary features that can be found at the mouths of rivers in other parts of Britain, including:

- a wide channel – up to 2 km
- sand and mud banks – Abernethy Bank
- some areas of marsh – in square 2119
- channels of deeper water – North Deep.

On reaching this tidal part of the river, a river's flow is reduced. The river loses much of its energy to transport its load and deposits it as sand and mud. These estuaries are difficult to navigate and to bridge, but they are good wildlife habitats. The River Earn has many features of a river in the lowlands (Source 4). Notice the big meander loop through squares 1718 and 1717 (Source 3). The black dashes marked around its edges show the levées. Settlements are larger than those in the uplands, but the danger of flooding means that they were carefully sited towards the edge of the floodplain where the risk of flooding was lower. The location of Abernethy is an example of this.

Source 4 | **Floodplain of the River Earn**

Flood plain and delta
the River Ganges

The source of the River Ganges is in the Himalayas. The Ganges flows across its floodplain for over 1500 km through northern India. The Ganges delta is found at the mouth of the river as it flows into the Bay of Bengal. The Indian city of Calcutta lies on the western side of the delta, but most of the delta is in Bangladesh (Source 1).

Within the zone covered by the floodplain and delta of the Ganges live some 10 per cent of the total world population. This area is one of the most densely populated parts of the world (see unit 9.1). Most people living here are farmers for whom rice is the main food crop.

The **monsoon** climate brings summer rain, which fills up the River Ganges (Source 2). For centuries the Ganges flooded the land around it between July and October. Each flood left another layer of fertile silt so that there is a great thickness of very rich and easy to work alluvial soils. Today a number of dams control the flooding of the river and supply water for winter crops. There is a neat landscape of tiny fields from which the farmers try to gain the highest possible output by hard work and by using high yielding varieties of rice, wheat and maize seeds (Source 3).

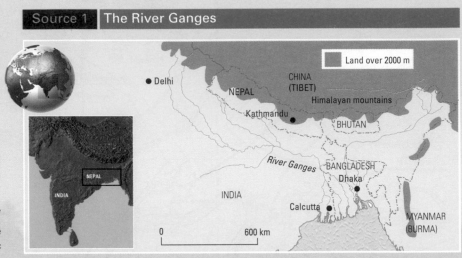

Source 1 The River Ganges

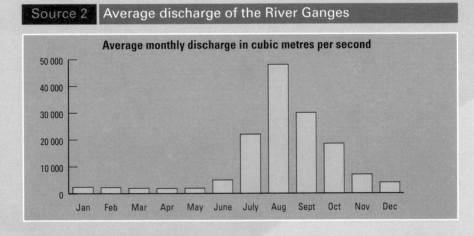

Source 2 Average discharge of the River Ganges

Average monthly discharge in cubic metres per second

Source 3 The Ganges floodplain is intensively farmed

Fact File | The Ganges delta

The delta is an example of a landform of river deposition. The physical features of the delta are labelled on the map and the reasons for the formation of the delta are written below.

Formation of a delta

1 The Ganges carries a large load of sediment.
2 The flow is slowed down by meeting the denser sea water.
3 Sediment is deposited faster than the tides can remove it.
4 River flow is blocked by so much deposition that the river splits up into distributaries.
5 Distributaries deposit sediment over a wide area, extending new land into the sea.

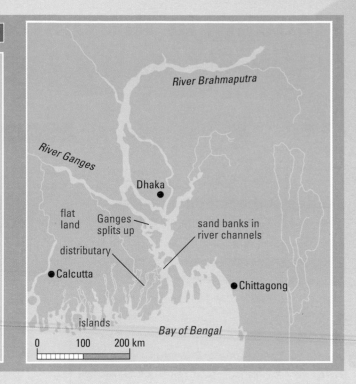

The *advantage* of the Ganges delta to the people of Bangladesh is that the land is very fertile. The silty soils are also easy to work. All the land is low lying (Source 4). There is water in the channels for irrigation during the dry season so that two or three crops can be grown. Many people can be fed each year.

The *disadvantage* is that the Bangladeshis live in a hazardous physical environment. The risk of being flooded is always present and many people have died. There are so many wide rivers to cross that land transport is slow and difficult. Access for ships is not easy because many channels are blocked by sand and mud. A wet environment in the tropics is a breeding ground for many diseases. Perhaps worst of all, Bangladesh is at the mercy of people living further up river. Nepal has cleared a lot of its forests; the higher rates of runoff in the mountains near the source have increased the severity of floods in Bangladesh at the river's mouth. India also uses the river for disposal of its waste products.

Source 4 | View of the Ganges delta

Flooding in the United Kingdom
the River Ouse

The River Ouse in Yorkshire floods during most winters. The floods in 1991 were worse than usual.

Causes of the flooding

The River Ouse has many tributaries originating in the higher parts of the Pennines where precipitation is high. In 1991, there was a month of heavier than average rainfall in the Pennines, followed by heavy snowfall. When the snow melted, the ground was already saturated. This meant a great runoff into the Pennine rivers, which transported more water into the River Ouse than its channel could hold (Sources 1, 2 and 3).

Source 1 Causes of the Ouse floods

Flood prevention measures

Embankments and flood walls line the sides of the River Ouse. The flood prevention scheme designed to protect the main commercial properties cost £8 million. Unfortunately, the flat, low-lying nature of the Vale of York near to the tidal part of the River Ouse means that freedom from flooding can never be guaranteed, even after spending millions of pounds.

Source 2 Newspaper report

ARMY CALLED IN TO RESCUE STRANDED RESIDENTS

York, 26 February 1991

Soldiers, equipped with aluminium boats, were called in to help residents stranded in flood-stricken York. The River Ouse was 4.5 metres higher than normal. Houses, shops and offices next to the river are still under water. More than 70 residents had to be evacuated. 'The streets were like canals,' said one of the army officers. At high tide yesterday the Ouse broke its banks south of York covering farmland, blocking roads and disrupting train services. The forecasters believe the worst is now over. Mopping up the water and clearing the mud out of their homes will be the next task for the unlucky residents.

Source 3 Floods in York

Source 1	Kielder reservoir: for water supply and recreation

Fact File	Kielder reservoir
Construction period	7 years
Number of trees felled	1 500 000
Height of dam wall	50 metres
Length of dam wall	1.2 km
Surface area of Kielder Water	1084 hectares
Supply capability	up to 1.2 million m³ of water a day
Length of shoreline created	43 km

Source 2	The distribution of Kielder water

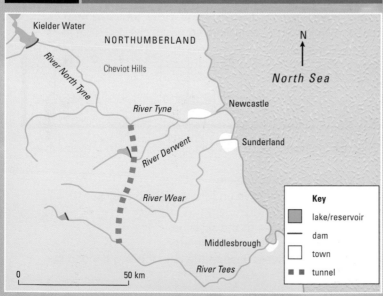

Kielder reservoir in Northumberland, which opened in 1982, is the largest artificial lake in western Europe (Source 1). It is over 10 km long and contains 190 million litres of water.

It was built as a water store to supply industry, particularly companies such as ICI and British Steel, located on Teesside, which were expected to expand.

The site selected in the Cheviot hills was chosen for several reasons.

- It has a large flat-bottomed valley with steep sides.
- The area has a high annual rainfall (1370 mm per year).
- It is a sparsely populated area – only a few families needed to be moved out when the dam was finished and the north Tyne valley was ready to be flooded.
- The land was marginal in quality, and could only be used for forestry and rough grazing.

Who uses the water?

While the reservoir was being constructed, the steel and chemical industries went into decline and did not need Kielder Water. However, Source 2 shows how the water can be distributed to all the main centres of population in north-east England by both rivers and pipelines. The presence of Kielder Water has meant that there have been no hosepipe bans or restrictions on water use in north-east England, even in the summer drought of 1995. Indeed water is exported – both to the Middle East and to Yorkshire. After the water shortages in Yorkshire in 1995, Yorkshire Water is paying for an extension of the pipeline south of the River Tees.

1 a Draw a labelled diagram to show the main features of the hydrological cycle.
  b Explain the differences between each of the following pairs:
    i evaporation and precipitation
    ii runoff and groundwater flow
    iii interception and percolation.
  c What is meant by evapo–transpiration?
  d Give the reasons why trees and impermeable rocks decrease the amount of runoff in the drainage basin.
  e Name two features of a drainage basin which favour a large amount of runoff. Explain why.

2 a State two ways in which the long profile of the river in the uplands is different from that in the lowlands.
  b Name and describe the ways in which the river is likely to transport the following:
    i pebbles and boulders
    ii sand and silt.
  c Make notes on the four different processes of river erosion.
  d i Name an example of a waterfall.
    ii State the different kinds of rock which are needed for a waterfall to form.
    iii What is a plunge pool? How is it formed?

3 a Describe how a river changes when it reaches the lowlands.
  b i Name two features formed by river deposition.
    ii Explain why rivers deposit their load in the lowlands.
  c With the aid of labelled diagrams, explain the formation of meanders and ox-bow lakes.

4 a Explain when and why rivers flood.
  b Describe as many disadvantages of flooding as you can.
  c The values below give the average amount of water in a European river at different times of year.
    i Plot these monthly amounts of water on a bar graph.
    ii In which season of the year is this river most likely to flood?
    iii The source for this river is high in the mountains. How does this help to explain the season in which the river is likely to flood?

Months	J	F	M	A	M	J	J	A	S	O	N	D
Amount of water (cubic m)	500	450	620	700	750	820	900	840	650	580	550	530

5 a Draw a labelled diagram to show one way in which people try to prevent river floods.
  b With reference to the River Rhône in France:
    i describe the type of work people have undertaken along the river to prevent flooding
    ii state and explain three advantages of the scheme.
  c How can people be one of the causes of river floods?
  d Explain why people live close to rivers despite the risk of being flooded out.

6 a Use the OS map on page 32 to answer the following.
  i Imagine you are walking between points A and B. Describe the changes in relief (shape of the land) you would notice on your walk.
  ii How many square kilometres of the land are used for coniferous woodland?
  iii Suggest reasons why trees are a common type of land use in an area such as this.
  iv Name five different land uses shown in square 9153.
 b Use the OS map on page 33 to answer the following.
  i Draw a sketch map of the River Tay estuary to the east of easting 20. Show and label on your map four physical features commonly found in a river estuary.
  ii Suggest the advantages and disadvantages of this river estuary for shipping. Use map evidence to support your answer.

7 In order to use the flooding of the Ouse in 1991 as a case study for river flooding, use page 36 to make brief notes using the headings:
 i causes of the flooding
 ii effects of the flooding
 iii flood protection measures used.

8 a Look at Source 1.
  i Make a frame and draw a field sketch of the photograph.
  ii Explain how the features shown on the photograph are formed by river erosion.
 b Source 2 shows where the photograph was taken and the area surrounding it.
  i Describe the physical attractions of the area for tourist visitors.
  ii Name two tourist facilities which have been provided.
  iii Suggest why the point marked **Z** could make a good site for a hydro-electric power station.

Source 1	The Iguaçu Falls

Source 2	Map of the Iguaçu Falls

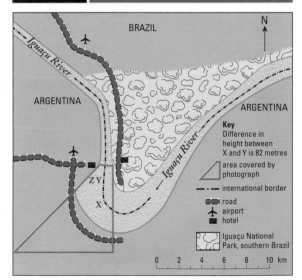

Key
Difference in height between X and Y is 82 metres
△ area covered by photograph
—·— international border
▰▰ road
✈ airport
■ hotel
Iguaçu National Park, southern Brazil

0 2 4 6 8 10 km

1 River systems and processes

Water is constantly being recycled. This creates a system of inputs, flows and outputs known as the hydrological cycle. The main input is precipitation. The main surface flow which supplies rivers with water is runoff. Some water infiltrates into the ground where it may be stored for some time before supplying surface rivers.

2 The river and its valley in the uplands

The river undertakes vertical erosion by processes such as abrasion, attrition, corrosion and hydraulic action. As a result, distinctive landforms, such as steep-sided V-shaped valleys, interlocking spurs, waterfalls and gorges are formed.

3 The river and its valley in the lowlands

The river undertakes lateral erosion on the outside of its bends to form river cliffs and meanders. There is much deposition of load to form landforms such as floodplains, levées and deltas.

4 River floods

A lot of rain, or very heavy rain, or melting of snow and ice, may lead to so much surface runoff that not all of the water can be held in the river channel. As soon as the river leaves its channel, it floods. Floods not only cause disruption, but also can be costly, leading to loss of life, property and crops.

People attempt to prevent rivers from flooding and they often try to manage rivers for benefits such as water supply, irrigation, HEP and shipping. There are many advantages which result from living close to rivers especially in the lowland areas, despite the flood risk. The fertile silt provides good soil for agriculture.

5 A river and its valley: the River Tay

In the uplands, the valley of the River Tay is high above sea level and steep sided, suggesting that vertical erosion is important. In the lowlands, the Rivers Tay and Earn have formed a wide floodplain, suggesting the greater importance of lateral erosion and deposition. In the estuary, many sand and mud banks are exposed at low tide.

6 Flood plain and delta: the River Ganges

The sides and the mouth of the River Ganges offer great opportunities for farming and settlement. They are one of the most densely populated parts of the world. However, they are a challenging environment because of the ever-present risk of flooding.

7 Flooding in the United Kingdom: the River Ouse

The River Ouse regularly floods in and around the city of York. It is a useful case study for looking at the causes and effects of river flooding.

8 Water supply: the Kielder reservoir

This case study shows how the upper part of a river basin may be managed to the benefit of the region lower down the valley. As with many multi-purpose schemes, there is one main advantage which is water supply in this example, and other advantages such as for recreation and tourism.

Coasts

The sea has created this natural arch at Durdle Door in Dorset.

The power of the sea

The coastline is a like a battle zone. It is here that the sea comes into direct contact with the land. Powerful waves crash against the rocks and cliffs and help to shape beaches. A complex set of processes allows the sea to erode the land, transport the eroded material and deposit it elsewhere. A series of coastal landforms are created – some of them by **erosion**, others by **deposition** (Source 1).

The nature of the waves (Source 2) determines whether landforms along a coastline are likely to be erosional or depositional.

Coastal erosion

Destructive waves are responsible for many spectacular landforms, including **cliffs**, **arches** and **stacks** like those in Source 3. Many different processes help to form and shape these landforms.

Source 1	Coastal landforms of erosion and deposition

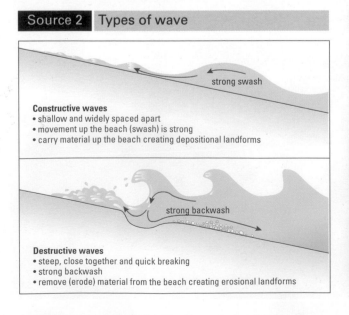

Source 2	Types of wave

strong swash

Constructive waves
• shallow and widely spaced apart
• movement up the beach (swash) is strong
• carry material up the beach creating depositional landforms

strong backwash

Destructive waves
• steep, close together and quick breaking
• strong backwash
• remove (erode) material from the beach creating erosional landforms

Source 3	Landforms caused by coastal erosion

Erosion occurs when powerful waves crash against the foot of a cliff. The waves hurl sand, shingle and pebbles against the cliff. This scrapes the rocks on the cliff in a process called **abrasion** which cuts a notch between the high and low water marks (Source 4A). The waves also trap air under pressure and this causes large pieces of rock to break off. This is called **hydraulic pressure.** The cliff retreats as the notch gets bigger and the overhanging rock collapses.

Harder rocks usually form cliffs. Softer rocks are more easily eroded, and wear back more quickly. Cliffs tend to stand out as **headlands.** When waves approach headlands they are bent or refracted. As a result they attack the headlands on three sides (Source 4B). Weaknesses in the rock will be eroded first, with small sea caves being formed. If the waves break through on both sides of the headland they form an arch. When the roof of the arch collapses an isolated tower of rock called a stack is left. This will eventually be worn away.

Source 4 Coastal processes

cliff retreats

original position of cliff

wave cut notch

high water mark

low water mark

wave cut platform

A Cliff erosion

softer rock

harder rock

stack

arch

waves attack weaknesses in rock cutting sea caves and arches

B Headland erosion

longshore drift

swash

backwash

direction of incoming waves

C Longshore drift

Source 5 Orford Ness, Suffolk: view of the growing spit

lagoon

end of spit

movement of beach sediment

Coastal deposition

The same waves that erode cliffs also carry the pebbles and sands from which most beaches are formed. These are known as **constructive waves.** The pebbles and sands are the remains of eroded cliff faces. Waves carry this material along the coast by a process called **longshore drift** (Source 4C).

The waves approach the shore at an angle. The **swash** pushes the sand and pebbles up the beach at the same angle. Then, the **backwash** flows back at right angles to the sea, carrying some of the pebbles and sand with it. In this way, the sand and pebbles are moved along the beach in a series of 'zig zags'.

Sometimes the shoreline changes direction. When this happens, the sand and pebbles continue to be pushed along by longshore drift. They now form a new beach roughly parallel to the shore called a **spit.** This is what is happening at Orford Ness in Source 5 (see also Unit 3.5).

Spits continue to grow in a series of curves of sand and pebbles. As in the case of Orford Ness, spits may divert rivers or lock up **lagoons** of water between them and the main shoreline. As the spit grows it may find an offshore island which it will join. This new landform is called a **tombolo.**

Cliff erosion

Burton Cliff in Dorset (Source 1) is made of sandstone which has been laid down in a number of layers or **strata**. The sandstone is hard and resists wave erosion. The effect of wave action is seen in the **wave attack zone,** which causes the cliff to be undercut. This is why there is a marked cliff overhang, resulting in such a steep cliff being formed.

When waves attack, they do most damage at the weakest points. These are between each layer of sandstone. This is where the most marked **wave cut notch** is seen. Undercutting means that large blocks of the cliff will collapse. This debris can be seen as the **rock platform.**

Here, the backwash of the waves is stronger than the swash, so smaller pieces of debris are removed from the foot of the cliffs. This is why there is such a narrow beach beneath the cliff.

Within the space of just 500 metres, Burton Cliff turns into Burton Beach. The map (Source 2) shows how close these two coastal features are to each other.

| Source 1 | Burton Cliff, Dorset |

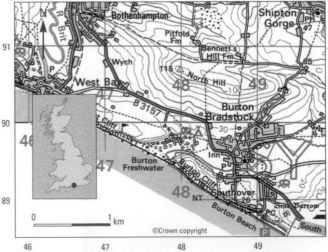

cliff overhang

wave attack zone

wave cut notch

rock platform

narrow beach

| Source 2 | Map showing Burton Cliff and Burton Beach |

| Source 3 | Burton Beach |

gentle slope

Burton cliff

wide beach

slumped clay

At Burton Beach (Source 3) there is a wide beach of fine sand and shingle. This has been moved from the foot of Burton Cliff by longshore drift. Here the swash of the waves is becoming stronger and the backwash weaker. The low cliff made of clay has slumped into a gentle slope.

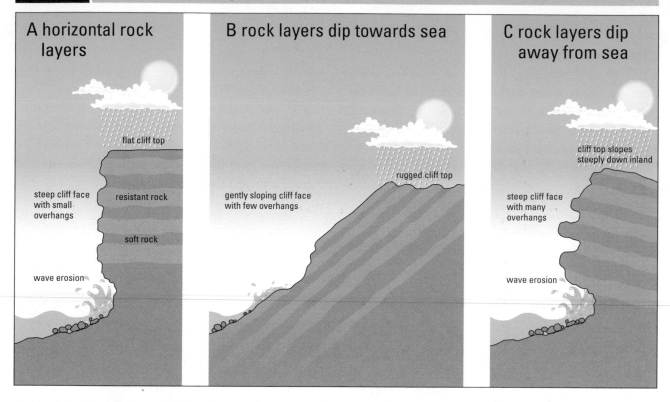

Behind the beach is a cliff, but it is quite low and not as steep as Burton Cliff. In fact, the material making the cliff has slumped down on to the beach. The land here is made of clay. The cliff has not been eroded by the sea at all. Instead, rain falling on the clay has made it **saturated**. When this happens the cliffs become unstable and begin to slump. The sea then carries away the clay that has been washed down on to the beach.

Wave action is not the only process shaping cliffs. The cliffs are also shaped by the actions of rain, ice, heat and wind. These actions are called **sub-aerial** weathering and erosion. In Source 4, the top of the cliffs is being weathered and eroded by sub-aerial actions. Only lower down the cliff does wave action take over.

Most rock is laid down as **sedimentary rock**. In the past, the seas covered much of the present land. Beneath these seas layer upon layer of sediments have been deposited. These sediments were hardened into rock by the pressure of overlying sediments. Some rock, such as sandstone, became very hard. Other rock, such as clay, remained soft.

When the rock was pushed up out of the sea it was usually tilted one way or another. The effect of this is seen in Source 4. A series of hard and soft rock layers are tilted towards or away from the sea, or may be left horizontal.

Sub-aerial weathering and erosion break up and remove the soft rock faster than the hard, resistant rock. If the rock layers are horizontal the weathering and erosion act equally across the layers of rock. If not, then the alternating weathering of hard and soft rock creates an uneven top surface of the cliff (Source 4B).

Lower down the cliff face, the waves are also affected by the lie of the rock layers. If the layers are horizontal (Source 4A) the cliff face will be steep with overhanging ledges – like Burton Cliff. If the layers dip towards the sea (Source 4B) the cliff face will have a gentle slope. If the layers dip away from the sea (Source 4C) there will be an uneven and steep cliff face.

Building beaches

The beach store

Beaches are made up of all the material lying between high water and low water marks. This material is known as the **beach store**. Source 1 shows how the beach store is built. There are four main sources of beach store:

- at A, erosion of the cliff is providing broken rock for the beach

- at B, longshore drift is carrying sand and small pebbles from the cliff to the main beach
- at C, **constructive waves** are pushing the sand and pebbles up the beach to make it higher and wider.
- at D, the river mouth is providing fine muds and gravels to add to the beach store.

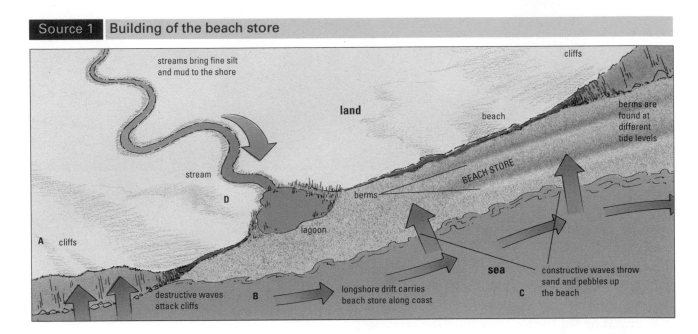

Source 1 Building of the beach store

streams bring fine silt and mud to the shore

cliffs

land

beach

berms are found at different tide levels

stream

BEACH STORE

D

berms

A cliffs

lagoon

sea

constructive waves throw sand and pebbles up the beach

destructive waves attack cliffs

B

longshore drift carries beach store along coast

C

Source 2 shows a typical beach store at Slapton Sands in south Devon. The shape of the beach can be clearly seen. It rises in a series of ridges, called **berms**. These ridges are built by constructive waves pushing the pebbles up the beach. If there is a very high tide the berm will be created high up the beach. Lower berms will be created nearer the water from constructive waves during lower tide levels.

Source 2 Slapton Sands, south Devon

Slapton Bay

berms

Start Bay

Source 3 | Start Bay, south Devon

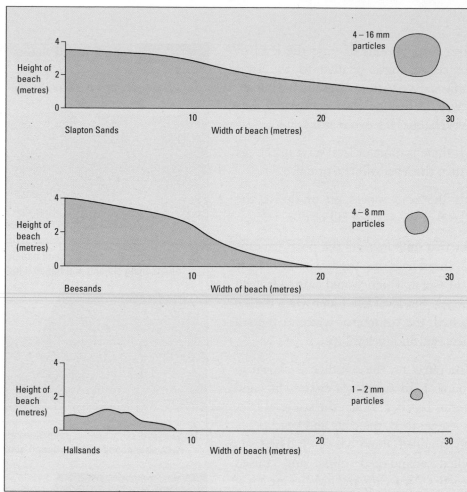

The changing beach

Source 3 shows the long beach of Start Bay on the south Devon coast. This beach runs north from Start Point to Pilchard Cove. The diagrams alongside the photograph show the size and shape of different beaches along the bay. Not only do the beaches become higher and wider from south to north, but the pebbles lying on them become larger. Why do these beaches change from south to north?

At Hallsands, to the south, the weathering and erosion of the cliff face is providing the beach store (as at A in Source 1). The waves are breaking down the rocks into pebbles. Then, as fast as they collect, the pebbles are being carried along the beach by longshore drift. So there is only a small beach, made up of a few pieces of unbroken rock and a thin covering of fine sand.

At Beesands, halfway along Start Bay, the picture is different. Here, a small stream is bringing fine muds and gravels down to the beach. The pebbles being moved along the beach have blocked the mouth of the stream, which empties into a small lagoon (D on Source 1). The beach here is wider and higher than Hallsands with larger pebbles.

The widest and highest beach, with the largest pebbles, is found at Slapton Sands. This beach catches all the pebbles which are being brought from the south. The headland cliffs of Pilchard Cove stop their further movement along the coast. Here are found all the very largest pebbles which are thrown up on to the beach by constructive waves.

Changing sea levels

Over long periods of time the level of the sea changes relative to the land surface. Every time there is a change, new cliffs and beaches are created. Sea level changes for two reasons.

1 If there is more or less water in the sea then the level will rise or fall.

2 If the land moves up or down, the level of the sea will fall or rise.

For two million years the polar ice caps advanced over the seas and land. The ice held water which would normally feed the sea. Sea level fell. Later when the ice melted, the volume of water in the sea increased and its level rose.

The effect on the coastline is shown in Source 1. In A, the sea erodes cliffs and creates beaches. When the sea level falls, as shown in B, the cliffs and beaches are left stranded above sea level. These are called abandoned cliffs and **raised beaches.** New cliffs and beaches are cut at the new sea level.

When the sea level rises again it will cover the new beaches and cliffs, creating a drowned coast. If the level does not return to its original place, there will be raised beaches and old cliff lines remaining above the sea level, as shown in C.

Rias and fiords

When the sea level rises, as we have seen, it creates a drowned coast. Sea water floods into estuaries and inlets. This happened in southern England when the glaciers melted at the end of the last Ice Age. Many drowned river valleys, known as **rias,** were created in Devon and Cornwall. This is what has happened in the case of the valley near Port Quin in Cornwall (Source 2).

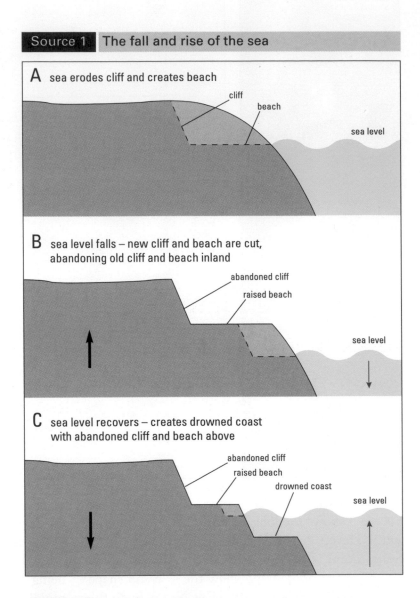

Source 1   The fall and rise of the sea

A sea erodes cliff and creates beach

cliff
beach
sea level

B sea level falls – new cliff and beach are cut, abandoning old cliff and beach inland

abandoned cliff
raised beach
sea level

C sea level recovers – creates drowned coast with abandoned cliff and beach above

abandoned cliff
raised beach
drowned coast
sea level

Source 2   Small ria near Port Quin, Cornwall

Source 3A Fiord in Scotland

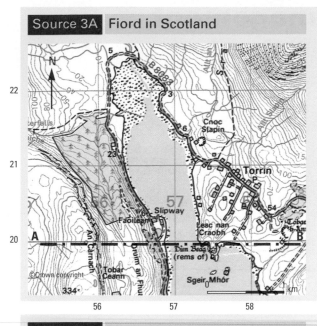

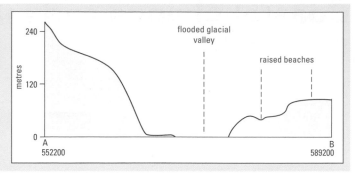

In other parts of Britain, where ice cut into valleys which were later flooded (Source 3A), **fiords** were formed. These are drowned glaciated valleys and differ from rias (Source 3B).

Source 3B Ria in Devon

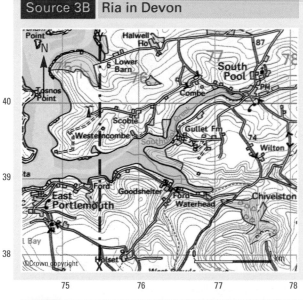

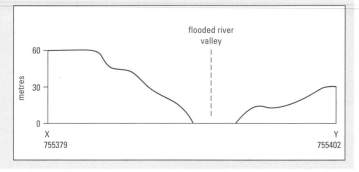

Source 4 Farmers make use of a raised beach above a fiord

In Scotland, events since the Ice Age have been more complicated. During the Ice Age glaciers cut deep valleys. The ice sheets were so thick that the land on which they rested was depressed. Sea level had already fallen. When the ice melted, the sea level rose and began cutting beaches and cliffs. Relieved of the weight of the ice, the land began to rise back to its old level. It carried up with it the new beaches and cliffs cut by the sea. The scene in north-west Scotland (Source 4) shows a raised beach lifted away from the sea by this post-glacial uplift of the land. This is a typical fiord coastline.

The increase in temperatures which is resulting from global warming may cause the polar ice caps to melt more rapidly. This will lead to another rise in sea level drowning many coastal landforms seen today.

Coastal change and management
the Suffolk coast

The Suffolk coastline is changing as a result of the powerful effects of the sea. The effects are both constructive and destructive. Cliffs are being eroded along one part of the coast, and the material is carried by longshore drift and deposited as a pebble spit further south.

Change: the building of Orford Ness

Orford Ness is a coastal spit in East Anglia (Source 1). The spit has been built up from beach store eroded to the north, around Dunwich, and further north up the coast. The Rivers Alde and Ore have been deflected southwards by the growth of the spit, the end of which lies off Shingle Street.

The spit is still growing in a southerly direction (Source 2). Destructive waves approach the land from the northeast, where the greatest **fetch** (the distance over the sea that the wind has blown) is to be found.

At Dunwich there are low cliffs made of soft sands. These sands are eroded by storm waves and are carried south by longshore drift. Shingle and pebbles also move southwards. Only the very fine sands are brought back north by the actions of the weaker longshore current. These are the reasons why the beach store particles become larger further south along the spit.

At Thorpeness the coastline changes direction from south to south-west. The sand and shingle have continued to be moved south. Aldeburgh was on the mouth of the River Alde until the spit began to deflect the river south over 1000 years ago.

Now, the spit near Aldeburgh is being used by the waves to provide beach store for the further extension of the spit. There are real fears that the present beach may be removed. **Groynes** and **rip-rap walls** have been built to try to stop this further erosion.

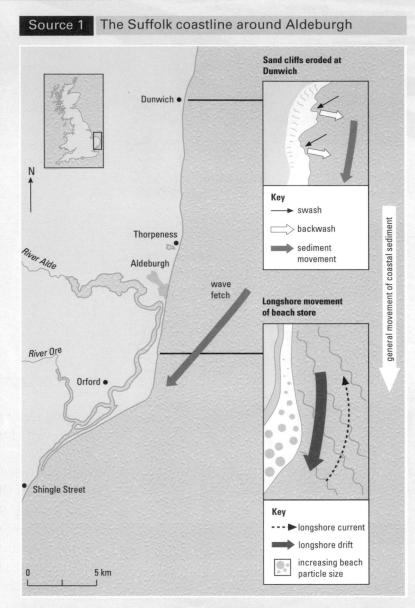

Source 1   The Suffolk coastline around Aldeburgh

Source 2   Orford Ness, Suffolk

Source 3 Looking south from Dunwich

Problems and solutions

The cliffs at Dunwich are being eroded (Source 3). There has been no attempt to stop this. Many people believe that the only effective way to stop erosion is to allow the waves to create a new beach. This would mean losing some of the shore and, perhaps, the village of Dunwich itself.

Source 4 Looking south from Aldeburgh – groynes

Aldeburgh is the main town along this stretch of coast. As the beach dwindled away, groynes were built to stop the southward movement of sand and shingle. This is not always successful, as Source 4 shows. The lower levels of the groynes appear to be losing the battle.

Source 5 A rip-rap wall at Aldeburgh

Another approach to dealing with erosion along this coastline has been the building of rip-rap walls (Source 5). These aim to lessen the force of the destructive waves. As the waves break on the shore they fall against large boulders or concrete blocks. The many gaps in between the blocks absorb the energy of the waves.

Global warming and the Suffolk coast

Some scientists predict that sea levels will rise as the burning of fossil fuels (wood, coal, oil) warms up the atmosphere. This could lead to the melting of the polar ice caps and a gradual rise in sea level. Some say that sea level will rise by up to 1 metre in the next 100 years. Such a rise would drown many coastal beaches and estuaries around the world.

The East Anglian coast would suffer. Much of the coast behind the Orford Ness spit would be flooded and the Dunwich cliffs would completely disappear. Building and maintaining barriers like groynes and rip-rap walls would prove too costly – the coast would have to be abandoned to the sea, and the town of Aldeburgh and the surrounding villages would be lost.

Using a coastal area
Milford Haven

The landscape of the haven

Milford Haven in South Wales (Source 1) is a ria. As sea level rose after the last Ice Age, water drowned this wide river valley. From the shore, the land rises steeply as cliffs. Out in the water lie many stacks, like Stack Rock and Thorn Island.

This whole coast is a deep water coast. The waves from the Atlantic Ocean that pound the cliffs are very destructive. The high, rugged coastal cliffs provide a habitat for much wildlife. People visit the area to enjoy the scenery and to take advantage of the recreation opportunities offered by walking, rock climbing and watersports.

This valuable natural resource is under pressure. It is protected by the Pembrokeshire National Park Authority. The Authority is responsible for managing sites of special interest, such as woodlands and sand dunes. In addition there are a number of **nature reserves,** which were set up to protect the rare birds and mammals that use the coast.

Source 1   The use of Milford Haven

location of Milford Haven

N

Milford Haven

Stack Rock

Haven

jetty   jetty

Thorn Island

Milford

jetty   jetty   jetties

Key
- ⊙ oil refineries and terminal
- ▲ power station
- ---- Pembrokeshire coastal path
- ▮ Pembrokeshire Coast National Park
- ▮ rock platform
- cliffs
- beach deposits

0   3 km

Industry in the haven

The inlet of Milford Haven (Source 1) allows giant oil tankers to offload their cargoes in safe deep water harbours. To the west is the Atlantic Ocean which links Britain with the world's main oil producing countries.

The jetties stand out in the deep water so that the oil tankers can offload without fear of striking the many rocks beneath the surface. Some oil is processed in the large **oil refineries** that have grown up around the inlet. One such refinery is shown in Source 2. The rest of the oil is sent by pipeline or by smaller tankers to other refineries in Britain.

The oil refineries have encouraged the development of other industries including a power station. In the town of Milford Haven itself, businesses, such as shops, insurance offices and transport services, have grown up as employment in the oil industry has grown.

Disaster in the haven

In February 1996, the *Sea Empress*, a huge oil tanker, hit rocks and ran aground on its approach to Milford Haven (Source 3). The disaster could not have come at a worse time for the area, which at this time of year is visited by many species of birds such as gannets and red-throated divers before they fly north. Large stretches of the Pembroke coastline were affected by the spill including areas of National Park and Sites of Special Scientific Interest (SSSI) (see Unit 12.6).

Conserving the haven

The Pembrokeshire Coastal Path (Source 4) surrounds the inlet of Milford Haven. The path takes walkers past some of the most attractive coastal scenery in Britain and attracts visitors to the area all year round.

This is a wild coast and the path can be made unsafe either by sea erosion or by too many people trampling it. The Pembrokeshire Coast National Park Authority is responsible for repairs and maintenance of the path.

Source 4 Pembrokeshire Coastal Path

Source 2 An oil refinery looms over small villages in the haven

Source 3 An oil spill off Milford Haven

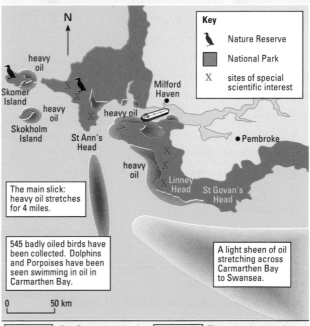

Key
- Nature Reserve
- National Park
- X sites of special scientific interest

heavy oil — Skomer Island — Skokholm Island — St Ann's Head — Milford Haven — Pembroke — Linney Head — St Govan's Head

The main slick: heavy oil stretches for 4 miles.

545 badly oiled birds have been collected. Dolphins and Porpoises have been seen swimming in oil in Carmarthen Bay.

A light sheen of oil stretching across Carmarthen Bay to Swansea.

0 — 50 km

Friday 16th *Sea Empress* runs aground while approaching Milford Haven. Starboard side ruptured. Towed back out to sea and held off St Ann's Head by tugs

Monday 19th Tanker runs aground again a few hundred yards from the cliffs. Oil spillage worsens. Weather conditions bad

Tuesday 20th The tanker has now lost some 50 000 tonnes of light crude oil, about a third of its cargo. Skomer and Skokholm Islands have been contaminated. At 7.30 pm last night (high tide), tugs tried to push her off the rocks. The plan was to ground the tanker again, further from the shore, so that she would be stable enough for another vessel to go alongside and retrieve her remaining cargo

53

Pollution
Italy's Adriatic coast

Mediterranean Europe is a popular destination for summer holidays. Each year millions of tourists from all over Europe travel down to the Mediterranean coast to enjoy the seaside in the sun. There are hotels and popular resorts from Venice south to Rimini.

The Adriatic Sea is an arm of the Mediterranean. As Source 1 shows, it is a narrow, enclosed sea. The River Po empties its waters into the sea south of Venice. As it flows through the lowlands between the Alps and Apennines, it passes through a rich farming area with many large towns.

Source 2 shows that visitors to the Adriatic coastline have to share the beach with sewage and other pollutants. Why does this happen?

The Po basin

The waters of the River Po are used as a dumping ground. About 37 per cent of Italian industry is located in the Po Basin, which has a population of 16 million people. Large quantities of industrial waste and domestic sewage are found in the coastal waters of the Adriatic. The heavy industry near Venice is one source of industrial pollution (Source 2). However, the biggest polluter is agriculture. The Po valley is Italy's largest stretch of flat land, so agriculture is a popular activity here. The farmers use fertilisers and pesticides heavily and some of these inputs eventually find their way into the rivers and ultimately into the shallow coastal waters.

| Source 1 | Coastal pollution in the Adriatic |

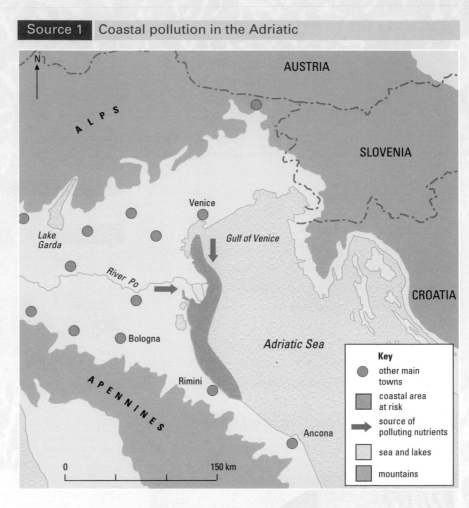

Key
- other main towns
- coastal area at risk
- source of polluting nutrients
- sea and lakes
- mountains

| Source 2 | Industry as well as farming sends pollutants to the Adriatic |

Source 3 | Eutrophication – the result of pollution

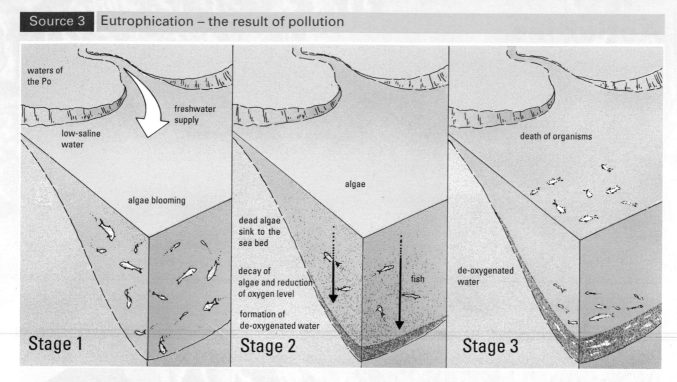

Two of the main culprits responsible for the green, slimy appearance of the waters of the Adriatic are phosphorus and nitrogen. These seep into the River Po from urban sewage works and the fertilisers used in the fields. Source 3 shows the effects which these chemicals have when they reach the shallow, warm waters of the Adriatic (Stage 1). Being nutrients, the phosphorus and nitrogen feed the minute, green water plants called algae which grow on the surface – this is what gives the coastal waters their green, slimy appearance.

Source 4 | Holidaymakers face thick slime on the beaches

When the algae die they fall to the sea bed, where they decay. The decaying algae remove the oxygen from the water (Stage 2). Without oxygen the other sea creatures cannot survive. Fish and plant life die, sinking to the bed, using up even more oxygen as they also decay. The result, as seen in Stage 3, is that the shallow coastal water loses all its oxygen. This is known as **eutrophication**. The waters are dead.

Cleaning up the River Po

Due to increased coastal polllution, holidaymakers are already declining in numbers (Source 4). Earnings from tourism are also falling. Few tourists will visit Italy's Adriatic coast and its resorts if the rivers, beaches and coastal waters are polluted and unpleasant. If the people living near the Adriatic wish to benefit from tourism in the future, they must spend money to stop the pollution.

They need to:

• reduce the use of fertilisers and pesticides
• build effective sewage works
• stop industrial and urban wastes being poured into the river systems.

One source of hope for the region's future is that the Po basin does now have a river authority which is responsible for improving water quality.

1 Look at the photograph on page 42.
   a Identify two landforms in the photograph.
   b State whether each landform was produced by erosion or deposition.
   c How would you expect this section of coast to have changed in ten thousand years time?

2 a The diagram (Source 1) shows five coastal landforms.
      i Name each landform.
      ii Explain how each landform is formed.
   b i What does the term 'fetch' mean?
      ii Explain why some waves are destructive and others are constructive.

Source 1 | Coastal landforms

3 a Explain the following terms using simple diagrams: wave attack zone; wave cut notch; cliff overhang; rock platform.
   b Explain why some cliffs are high with steep faces and others are low with gently sloping faces.

4 a i What does the term beach store mean?
      ii Describe four ways in which beach store is built up.
   b i Using a simple diagram explain why beaches become wider and higher and have larger particles, along some parts of a coast.
      ii Describe how beach berms are formed.

5 a Describe how the following features are formed: raised beach; abandoned cliff; drowned coast; ria; fiord.
   b Explain why there have been changes in the level of the land and sea in the last million years.
   c Describe the effects of global warming on coasts.

6 Study the map of 'Rivermouth' in Source 2. Rivermouth was once a thriving fishing harbour. Recent decline in fish stocks due to pollution and overfishing has resulted in little work for most of the fishing boats.

The town council wants to revive the fortunes of the area. Talks have been started between council members and the directors of a leisure company, who want to build a holiday camp and recreation centre.

Some council members are greatly opposed to the scheme, fearing that it would change the nature of the coastal area for the worse.

a Present a case for building the holiday camp and recreation centre. In your proposals you should:

- suggest a site for the centre
- locate routes for the access roads leading to the centre
- describe how this coastline can be used for leisure and recreation
- identify any parts of the coast which you would expect to be protected by the developers.

b Look critically at your proposals and put the case for the opponents of the scheme. Make detailed reference to the expected damaging impact on specific sites which you think, from map evidence, are worthy of conservation.

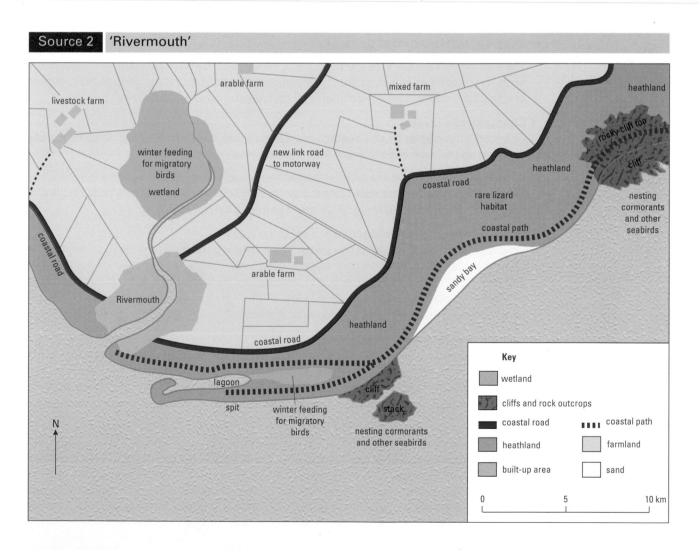

Source 2 'Rivermouth'

1 The power of the sea

Waves erode when the backwash removes more sediment than the swash is pushing onto the beach. The power of the wave is generated by the fetch.

Waves erode cliffs by abrasion and hydraulic pressure. They create a rock platform at the foot of cliffs, and mould the cliffs into headlands, arches and stacks.

Waves build beaches when the swash deposits more sediment than the backwash removes. Longshore drift shapes beaches into spits, tombolos or bays.

2 Cliff erosion

Hard, resistant rocks form steep cliffs; soft rocks create low, gentle cliffs. Wave-cut notches create cliff overhangs. Rock collapses onto the rock platform at the foot of the cliff. It is removed by wave erosion and transported by longshore drift.

Erosion by rain, ice, wind and heat shape that part of the cliff above the wave attack zone. The shape of this and the cliff face is affected by the angle of the rock strata.

3 Building beaches

The beach store is all the sediment on the beach. This beach store is gained from eroding cliffs, longshore movement, constructive surging waves and river deposits. It can be lost by the action of destructive plunging waves, the filling-in of estuaries, longshore movement and sand dune migration.

The size of the beach and of the particles of sand, shingle and pebbles of the beach store become greater in the direction of longshore movement. On large beaches, waves create ridges called berms. Each berm represents the different tide level.

4 Changing sea levels

Changes of the level of the sea against the land are caused by either a) polar ice cap advance and retreat, or b) rising or falling land levels.

If the sea level falls the old cliffs and beaches are left stranded as abandoned cliffs and raised beaches. If the sea level rises the valleys and cliffs will be part of a drowned coast. Rias are drowned river valleys; fiords are drowned glaciated valleys.

5 Coastal change and management: the Suffolk coast

Orford Ness is a coastal spit. The beach store is being moved from north to south. The cliffs and beaches to the north are being eroded away. There is no protection for the cliffs and Dunwich may be at risk. The beach at Aldeburgh is also at risk. Here groynes and rip-rap walls have been built to reduce erosion. In the future, global warming may cause sea levels to rise, which will affect many coastal areas.

6 Using a coastal area: Milford Haven

Milford Haven is a large ria. It has a natural deep-water harbour facing the busy North Atlantic Ocean. Along the shores are jetties where the oil tankers deliver their crude oil cargoes. Oil refineries and power stations line the shore. Rising from the shore are cliffs and hills, which provide wildlife havens and recreation and leisure opportunities for people.

7 Pollution: Italy's Adriatic coast

The Adriatic is a narrow enclosed sea. The River Po brings pollutants from towns and farms. These help algae to grow in the coastal zone south of Venice. The algae's growth is caused by eutrophication. The warm summer weather makes conditions worse because it encourages rapid algae growth. The heavy industry developed around Venice to the north adds further pollutants direct to the sea.

Ice landscapes

The Matterhorn (4505 m), a pyramidal peak in the Alps

Landscapes eroded by ice

In the last Ice Age, 2 million to 10 000 years ago, the climate was much colder than it is today. In the upland areas of the UK, the winter snow was retained all year. Each year more snow was added and it slowly compressed into ice. In some places, like north-west Scotland, the whole landscape was covered by huge ice sheets, as shown in Source 1. In some places the ice only filled the valleys, forming **glaciers.**

Today permanent ice is only found above the **snowline** in areas such as the Arctic and Antarctic and the higher parts of mountain ranges such as the Alps and Himalayas.

Ice sheets

These are huge masses of ice which move very slowly. At their edges there may be glaciers and in the sea they often form icebergs. As an ice sheet moves it scrapes and scratches the rock below. Areas of harder rock are rounded and smoothed. Areas with softer rocks are eroded to a greater depth forming basins which sometimes fill with water. These are called 'lochans' (Source 2). As the ice sheets melted and retreated they deposited all the material they had eroded. Huge quantities of **boulder clay** were laid down in the lowland areas.

Valley glaciers

Glaciers form in hollows on the sheltered sides of mountains. These are usually the north and north-east facing slopes in the northern hemisphere. As ice collects in a hollow, the pressure builds up. The ice bulges and begins to flow downhill. As it flows, it moves over obstacles, and splits occur called **crevasses.**

As the ice moves it erodes the landscape by the processes of **abrasion** and **plucking** (Source 3). The erosion produces many different features which are shown in Source 4.

Source 1 Glaciated landscapes in the UK

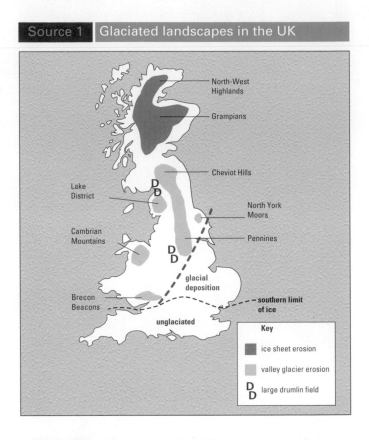

Source 2 Ice rounded hills, and lochans

Source 3 — Processes of glacial weathering and erosion

1 Abrasion—rocks and boulders in the base of the glacier act like a giant file scratching and scraping the rocks below

2 Plucking—the ice may freeze to the rock below and as the ice moves it pulls the rock away with it. This is very effective if the rocks have been loosened by freeze-thaw weathering.

3 Freeze-thaw weathering—extreme cold causes water to freeze in cracks in the rocks. As the water freezes it expands, causing the cracks to widen and the rock to break up. It helps to create arêtes and screes.

scree

3A Water collects in cracks and freezes.

3B The ice expands and cracks widen.

3C Rocks break up into angular blocks.

Source 4 — Features of glacial erosion

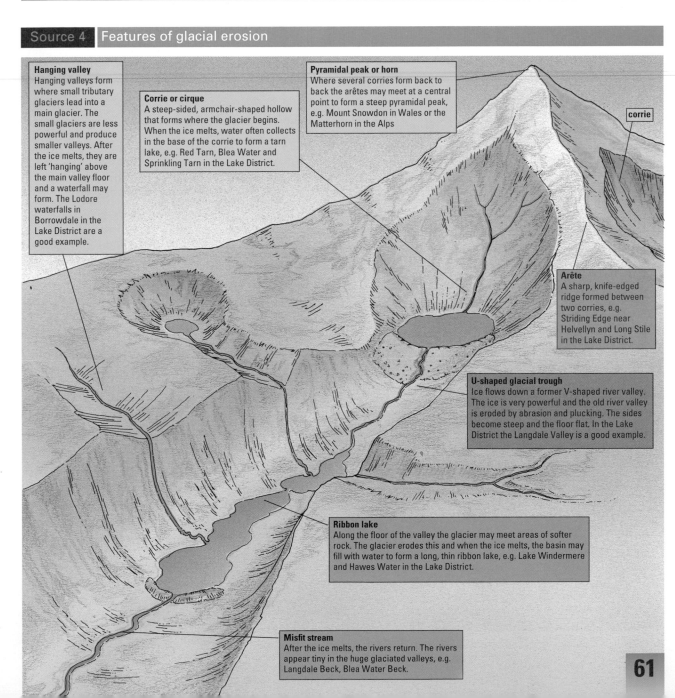

Hanging valley
Hanging valleys form where small tributary glaciers lead into a main glacier. The small glaciers are less powerful and produce smaller valleys. After the ice melts, they are left 'hanging' above the main valley floor and a waterfall may form. The Lodore waterfalls in Borrowdale in the Lake District are a good example.

Corrie or cirque
A steep-sided, armchair-shaped hollow that forms where the glacier begins. When the ice melts, water often collects in the base of the corrie to form a tarn lake, e.g. Red Tarn, Blea Water and Sprinkling Tarn in the Lake District.

Pyramidal peak or horn
Where several corries form back to back the arêtes may meet at a central point to form a steep pyramidal peak, e.g. Mount Snowdon in Wales or the Matterhorn in the Alps

corrie

Arête
A sharp, knife-edged ridge formed between two corries, e.g. Striding Edge near Helvellyn and Long Stile in the Lake District.

U-shaped glacial trough
Ice flows down a former V-shaped river valley. The ice is very powerful and the old river valley is eroded by abrasion and plucking. The sides become steep and the floor flat. In the Lake District the Langdale Valley is a good example.

Ribbon lake
Along the floor of the valley the glacier may meet areas of softer rock. The glacier erodes this and when the ice melts, the basin may fill with water to form a long, thin ribbon lake, e.g. Lake Windermere and Hawes Water in the Lake District.

Misfit stream
After the ice melts, the rivers return. The rivers appear tiny in the huge glaciated valleys, e.g. Langdale Beck, Blea Water Beck.

Glaciation in the lowlands

Glaciers pick up large amounts of eroded material or moraine. The moraine is transported by ice along glacial valleys to the lowland areas.

The moraine is given different names depending on where it is found (Source 1).

Source 1 | Types of moraine

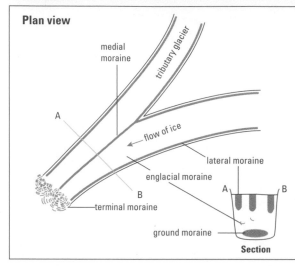

Plan view

- medial moraine
- tributary glacier
- A
- flow of ice
- B
- terminal moraine
- lateral moraine
- englacial moraine
- ground moraine
- A — B
- **Section**

Ground moraine – at the base, a result of abrasion and plucking of the valley floor

Lateral moraine – at the sides, a result of ice erosion of the valley sides and freeze thaw weathering on the bare rock above

Englacial moraine – in the ice. Rocks carried by meltwater over the surface and from rock falls are frozen into the ice

Medial moraine – forms at the junction of two lateral moraines where tributary glaciers meet

Terminal moraine – marks the furthest point the ice reached

Source 2 | Boulder clay in a moraine on the Isle of Arran, Scotland

As the climate warms up, the ice begins to melt. The glacier can no longer carry all the boulders, clay and sand it has picked up, so it begins to deposit material (Source 2). This usually happens in the lowland areas where the climate is warmer.

The deposited material is a mixture of **boulder clay** and very fine material called **rock flour**. Boulder clay is a mixture of sand, stones, clay and boulders. All the material is angular, not smooth and rounded like river sediments. Boulder clay covers large areas in England especially in East Anglia where it forms fertile soils which are good for crop growing.

Landforms of glacial deposition

The lowland areas affected by deposition have different landforms to the upland eroded landscapes (Source 3). There are moraines, drumlins and erratics.

Source 4 A huge erratic block in Yorkshire

Source 3 A landscape of glacial deposition

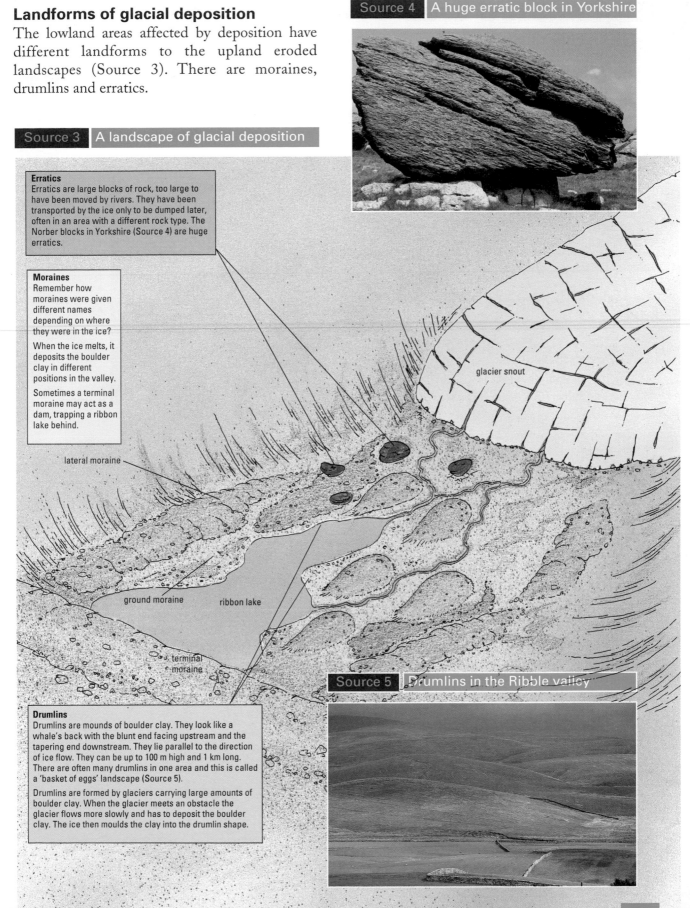

Erratics
Erratics are large blocks of rock, too large to have been moved by rivers. They have been transported by the ice only to be dumped later, often in an area with a different rock type. The Norber blocks in Yorkshire (Source 4) are huge erratics.

Moraines
Remember how moraines were given different names depending on where they were in the ice?

When the ice melts, it deposits the boulder clay in different positions in the valley.

Sometimes a terminal moraine may act as a dam, trapping a ribbon lake behind.

glacier snout

lateral moraine

ground moraine   ribbon lake

terminal moraine

Source 5 Drumlins in the Ribble valley

Drumlins
Drumlins are mounds of boulder clay. They look like a whale's back with the blunt end facing upstream and the tapering end downstream. They lie parallel to the direction of ice flow. They can be up to 100 m high and 1 km long. There are often many drumlins in one area and this is called a 'basket of eggs' landscape (Source 5).

Drumlins are formed by glaciers carrying large amounts of boulder clay. When the glacier meets an obstacle the glacier flows more slowly and has to deposit the boulder clay. The ice then moulds the clay into the drumlin shape.

A glaciated area
the Lake District

The Lake District lies in north-west England (Source 1). It has some of the most spectacular glacial scenery in Britain. During the Ice Age, glaciers developed on the higher slopes of the mountains especially on the colder north and north-east facing slopes. The glaciers eroded the rock by abrasion and plucking, forming deep hollows and huge U-shaped valleys (Source 2).

Hawes Water in the Lake District

Sources 3 and 4 show the area around Hawes Water in the Lake District. Hawes Water is a long, thin **ribbon lake** which fills the valley floor of the **glacial trough**. The lake formed after the ice had carved out an area of softer rock creating a depression. Source 2 shows the long profile of the glacial trough after the ice has melted. Notice how the upland areas have features formed by glacial erosion, while the lowlands have more depositional features. The large depression has also been filled with water to form the ribbon lake called Hawes Water.

Two small **corrie** tarns can be seen in Source 3, Small Water in the far left and the larger Blea Water Tarn to its right. Both these tarns lie in corries – large, armchair-shaped hollows carved out by the ice. From Blea Water Tarn a small beck (stream) flows down into Hawes Water. Notice how small the beck is in relation to the valley. It is a **misfit stream.** Can you see any more?

Between Blea Water Tarn and the large glacial trough to the right, called Riggindale, there is a knife edged ridge called an **arête**. The arête is called Long Stile. Behind Long Stile is another arête called High Street. Its highest point is 830 metres above sea level.

Source 1 The Lake District

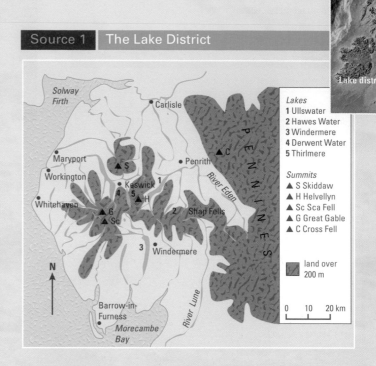

Lakes
1 Ullswater
2 Hawes Water
3 Windermere
4 Derwent Water
5 Thirlmere

Summits
▲ S Skiddaw
▲ H Helvellyn
▲ Sc Sca Fell
▲ G Great Gable
▲ C Cross Fell

land over 200 m

0   10   20 km

Source 2 Long profile of a glaciated valley

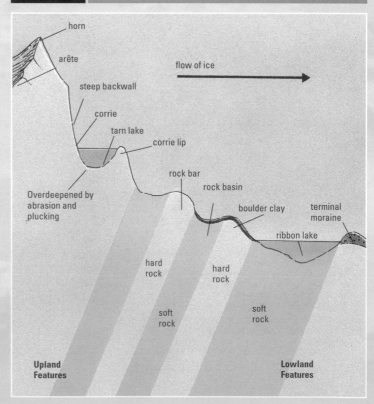

Today Hawes Water is at a higher level than it used to be. In 1929 the Manchester Corporation which owned the area built a small dam to raise the level and lengthen the lake to provide a water supply for Manchester. The village of Mardale with its dairy farms and pub was drowned as the reservoir filled up. Large coniferous woods were planted and the valley has completely changed.

In the Lake District valleys, and around the fringes, features produced by glacial deposition can also be found. Lake Windermere for example is dammed by a **terminal moraine** and many of the valleys contain deposits of boulder clay. There are **erratics** like the huge Bowder Stone in Borrowdale. In the Eden valley there are over 600 small oval hills all about the same size and shape and all in an area of 300 square km. This is a 'basket of eggs' landscape – a swarm of **drumlins** made up of boulder clay.

Source 3 | The area around Hawes Water

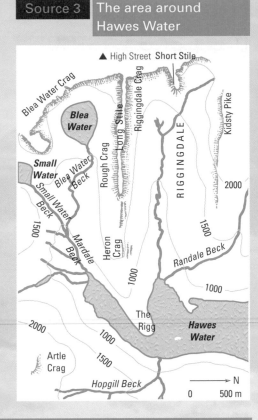

Source 4 | Aerial photograph of Blea Water Tarn

Human activity in a glaciated area
the Lake District

The Lake District is the workplace and home for many people as well as a temporary home for over 12 million visitors each year. In the Lake District there are opportunities to work in farming, forestry, water supply and service industries including tourism. Look carefully at Source 1 to find out more about the human activity in a Lake District valley.

Source 1 | **Work and leisure in a Lake District valley**

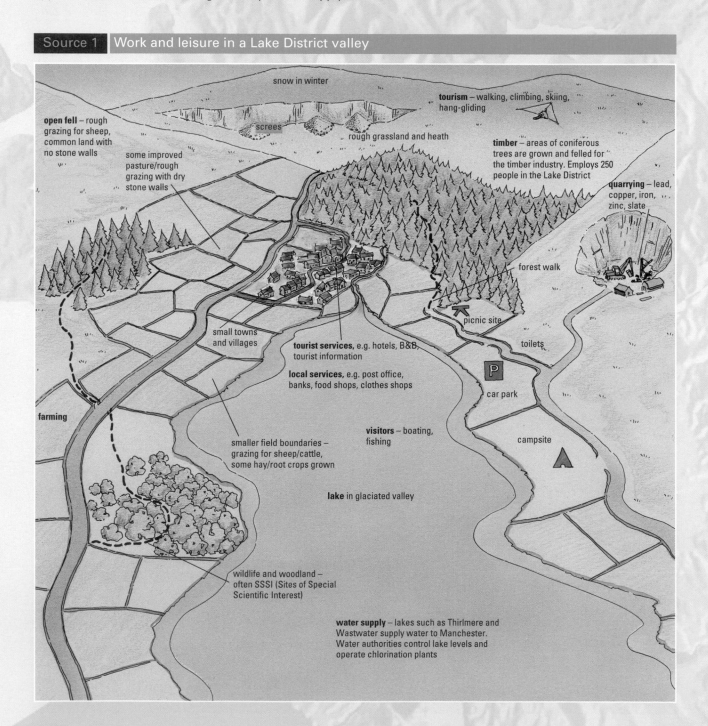

snow in winter

tourism – walking, climbing, skiing, hang-gliding

open fell – rough grazing for sheep, common land with no stone walls

screes

rough grassland and heath

timber – areas of coniferous trees are grown and felled for the timber industry. Employs 250 people in the Lake District

some improved pasture/rough grazing with dry stone walls

quarrying – lead, copper, iron, zinc, slate

forest walk

picnic site

small towns and villages

tourist services, e.g. hotels, B&B, tourist information

toilets

local services, e.g. post office, banks, food shops, clothes shops

car park

farming

visitors – boating, fishing

campsite

smaller field boundaries – grazing for sheep/cattle, some hay/root crops grown

lake in glaciated valley

wildlife and woodland – often SSSI (Sites of Special Scientific Interest)

water supply – lakes such as Thirlmere and Wastwater supply water to Manchester. Water authorities control lake levels and operate chlorination plants

| Source 2 | Problems and conflicts in the Lake District |

| Source 3 | Camping site near Windermere |

TAKE-AWAY THREAT TO AREA'S IMAGE

Fish and chips shops and hot-dog stands are spoiling the Lakeland. One of Britain's best landscapes is being cheapened. Planners need to be stricter.

'MAJOR IMPACT' FEAR OVER CHALET VILLAGE AT ENNERDALE

Building 40 timber chalets would destroy the character of the area. Plans by the Forestry Commission include a car park, service buildings and a swimming pool.

Problems and conflicts

The Lake District is an area of great beauty and a **National Park.** The National Park Authority works hard to try to conserve the environment and manage the area to allow visitors access without causing damage. In recent years (see Source 2) there have been problems and conflicts.

- Large numbers of visitors have caused traffic congestion.
- Footpaths are becoming badly eroded.
- There are also conflicts between the farmers, tourists and the National Park Authority.

People are worried that tourist developments are spoiling the area. For example large areas are used as camping and caravan sites (Source 3), and signposts clutter the verges. Source 4 shows the results of a questionnaire of 6000 groups of people visiting the Lake District. The table shows that the Windermere/Bowness area is least enjoyed because it is too crowded, too commercialised and too like a seaside resort. Some visitors also complain that the area lacks car parks and other facilities. How do you think the local people will react to plans for more facilities for tourists such as bypasses, holiday chalets and cable cars?

| Source 4 | Lake District visitors survey results |

Place no longer enjoyed	% no longer enjoying visit	Reasons					
		too commercialised	too crowded	like a seaside resort	too much traffic	not enough car parks	lack of facilities
Windermere/Bowness	26.2	616	914	103	49	15	3
Keswick	7.4	136	278	9	32	8	1
Ambleside	5.8	109	237	20	27	5	2
Coniston	1.0	12	20	3	3	1	3
Tarn Hows	0.7	10	25	1	5	1	3

1 Copy and complete the paragraph below about glacial erosion. The three missing words are plucking, abrasion and freeze thaw.

Rocks in the base of a glacier act like a giant file scraping away at the rocks below. This is called _____. Ice can freeze on to rocks and when the ice moves the rocks are pulled away. This is called _____. Above a glacier the bare rock slopes are sharpened by _____ weathering. This is when the water in cracks expands as it freezes causing the rocks to break up.

2 Study the block diagram (Source 1) and write a list of the features shown marked A to L.

3 Copy the diagrams of a corrie in Source 2.
   a Describe the main features of a corrie.
   b Add the following statements to your diagram to show how a corrie is formed.

   Water moves down the crack and freezes in the base of the corrie.

   Plucking and abrasion erode the corrie floor.

   The glacier rotates deepening the corrie.

   The glacier flows out of the corrie leaving a lip.

   Above the ice the rocks are shattered by freeze thaw weathering.

4 Study the pages about human activity in a glaciated area.
   a List five jobs that the tourist industry will create.
   b Using Source 2 and the text on page 67 describe some of the problems and conflicts between the tourists and the local people.
   c Using Source 4 on page 67, draw a bar graph to show the figures for the percentage of people no longer enjoying the visit.
   d Explain why some people no longer enjoy going to Windermere and Bowness.
   e Try to suggest some solutions to the problems.

Source 1 A glacial landscape

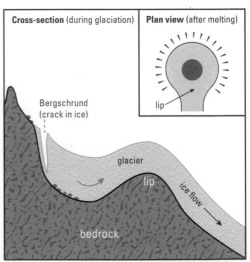

Source 2 Cross-section and plan view of a corrie

Cross-section (during glaciation) Plan view (after melting)

Bergschrund (crack in ice)

glacier

lip

ice flow

bedrock

lip

Source 3 OS extract of the area around Hawes Water in the Lake District

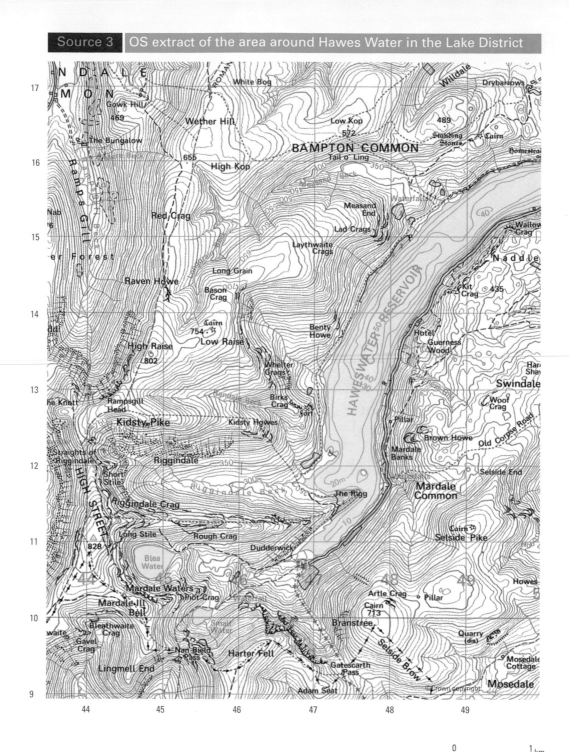

0 _____ 1 km

5 Study the OS map of the area around Hawes Water (Source 3).
  a Give the 4-figure grid reference for the parking area south of Hawes Water reservoir.
  b Give the 6-figure grid reference and the height of the highest point along High Street.
  c Name an example of a corrie tarn and give its grid reference.
  d There is often a small stream running from the corrie tarns. Name an example of one of these streams. Why are they often called 'misfit' streams?
  e Measure the width of Hawes Water reservoir along grid line 14.
  f What shape of valley is the reservoir in?
  g Write a few sentences to describe the human activities (past and present) shown by the map. Think about settlement, farming, forestry, tourism and water supply.

1 Landscapes eroded by ice

During the last Ice Age large parts of Britain were covered in snow and ice. North-west Scotland was totally submerged below huge ice sheets. The ice sheets scraped the ground forming ice-rounded hills and small lakes. Many valleys in upland areas like the Lake District had smaller valley glaciers.

Glaciers flowing down a valley erode the landscape by plucking and abrasion. They create many features such as U-shaped glacial troughs, corries, arêtes and pyramidal peaks. When the glaciers have melted, the rock basins are filled with water to form ribbon lakes. Corrie lakes or tarns may form in corries. The rivers start to flow again and they are called misfit streams.

2 Glaciation in the lowlands

The boulder clay which the glacier erodes is transported to the lowlands. Here the glacier will deposit the material as the warmer conditions cause the ice to melt. Some of the material is deposited in moraines, for example lateral and terminal moraines.

Other features of lowland glaciation are drumlins and erratics. Drumlins often form together giving a 'basket of eggs' landscape. Erratics are huge boulders of a different rock type in an area.

3 A glaciated area: the Lake District

The Lake District has spectacular glacial landscapes. The area around Hawes Water has many of the features of glacial erosion and deposition. Hawes Water is a ribbon lake, Blea Tarn is a corrie tarn and Long Stile is an arête. To the east of the Lake District the Eden valley is famous for its drumlin field.

4 Human activity in a glaciated area: the Lake District

Glaciated valleys are the home and workplace for many people. The main sources of employment are hill sheep farming, forestry, water supply, quarrying and service industries. The Lake District is also one of England's National Parks so many of the jobs are connected to tourism.

The annual influx of visitors brings both advantages in terms of jobs and money, and disadvantages. The visitors cause problems and conflicts with the local people, for example they cause litter and traffic congestion, footpaths are eroded and farmers' gates left open. Many people would like to see the numbers of visitors controlled and the introduction of schemes to reduce traffic problems.

Over 12 million people visit the Lake District each year. They wish to enjoy the spectacular scenery and escape the urban lifestyle. Many people go walking or climbing in the hills but many don't venture very far from the small towns and villages or their cars. The most popular areas like Windermere and Bowness have become 'honeypots'. They are always crowded. Even the visitors are saying they don't enjoy their visits any more. The tourists are destroying the very landscape they have come to enjoy.

Weather, climate and ecosystems

In West Africa and across the Atlantic Ocean the cloud associated with equatorial areas stands out clearly on this satellite image. The Mediterranean Sea and the Sahara Desert are clearly visible.

Measuring weather

It is important to study the weather because it affects so many human activities. Airlines and ships need accurate information, so do farmers, skiers, walkers and the general public.

The weather is the state of the **atmosphere** at a certain time and it may change from hour to hour. A weather forecast often mentions the temperature, wind, rainfall, pressure and humidity. These are the elements of the weather. Around Britain there are many meteorological stations where weather is measured by special equipment. Source 1 shows the layout of a weather station with the instruments which are used. Weather stations are sited away from tall trees and buildings so that they are not sheltered from wind, rain or sun.

Today, the use of modern electronic equipment such as computers and radar means that the weather can be recorded continuously and forecasts are more accurate.

Source 1   A weather station

Sunshine recorder
This records the hours of sunshine received in a day. This is the number of hours the sun actually shines, not just when it is light.

Maximum and minimum thermometer (Six's thermometer)

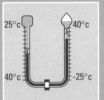

The thermometer contains alcohol and mercury and two metal indexes, one in each limb. When the temperature rises, the alcohol in the left-hand side expands and pushes the mercury up the right-hand side, which also pushes the index along. The maximum temperature is read from the bottom of the index in the right hand limb. When the temperature falls, the alcohol contracts and the mercury flows in the opposite direction, pushing the index along. The minimum temperature is read from the bottom of the index in the left-hand thermometer – notice the scale is reversed.

Wind speed and direction

Wind direction is measured by a wind vane. The rotating arm points to the direction from which the wind blows and the wind is named after this. So a westerly wind blows from the west.
Wind speed is measured by an anemometer. It has three or four cups on arms which rotate when the wind blows. The movement operates a meter which records the speed of the wind in kilometres per hour.

Wet and dry bulb thermometer (hygrometer)

The hygrometer records the relative humidity – the amount of water in the air. It has two ordinary thermometers but the bulb of one is wrapped in damp muslin. If the air is not saturated, water from the muslin evaporates and this cools the wet bulb thermometer. It records a lower temperature than the dry bulb. If the air is saturated there is no evaporation and the readings are the same. A small difference in readings means the humidity is high, a large difference means the humidity is low.

Stevenson screen

The Stevenson screen is a wooden box, painted white to reflect the sun. It has louvred sides to let the air circulate. It contains a maximum and minimum thermometer, and a wet and dry bulb thermometer, which all measure shade temperatures.

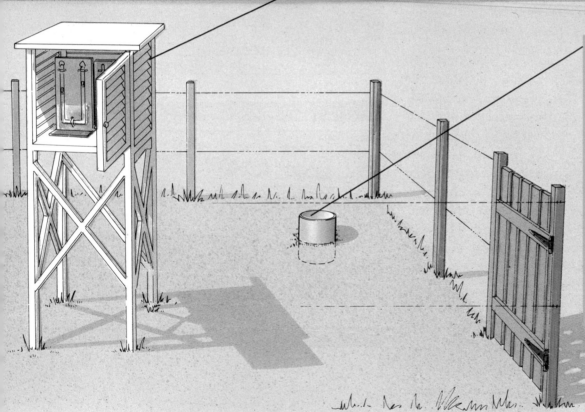

Rain gauge

Rainfall is measured in millimetres using a rain gauge. Rain falls into the funnel and collects in the glass jar below. After 24 hours the water is tipped into a measuring cylinder and the amount recorded. The rain gauge is in an open area with about 30 cm above the ground to stop splashing and to stop the sun evaporating moisture.

Air pressure

A barometer is used to measure air pressure in millibars. It can be located indoors since pressure is not affected by buildings. Inside the barometer, a small metal box contains very little air and its top moves very slightly as the air pressure changes. The movement is conveyed by a series of levers to a pointer which moves across graph paper recording the pressure changes.

Factors affecting climate

The **climate** is the average weather of an area. It is worked out by taking the average of the temperature and rainfall figures over a number of years.

The following factors affect the climate of an area.

Latitude

Polar regions are much colder than places near the Equator. This is due to the effect of **latitude** and the shape of the earth (Source 1). Places further away from the Equator receive less energy from the sun. In low latitudes:
- the sun's rays travel a shorter distance through the atmosphere
- the sun's rays are concentrated in a smaller area.

Maritime effect

Coastal areas are often warmer in winter but colder in summer than places further inland. This is due to the **maritime effect** (Source 2). The sea takes longer to heat up in the summer so the sea is colder than the land. Cool sea breezes form, so coastal areas are a few degrees colder than further inland in summer. In winter it takes longer for the sea to cool down, so the sea is warmer than the land. The west coast of the UK is particularly warm in winter because of the North Atlantic Drift, a warm ocean current.

Altitude

Uplands tend to be colder than lowlands due to the effect of **altitude** (Source 3). Temperature falls as altitude increases – usually by about 1°C every 160 metres. So a mountain 1600 metres high would be 10°C colder at the top than at sea level.

Prevailing winds

In the UK the **prevailing winds** are from the west. The west coast of the UK is in the path of the prevailing winds and so it tends to be much wetter than the east coast, which is more sheltered and in the **rain shadow** (Source 3).

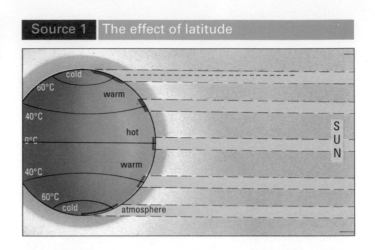

Source 1 | The effect of latitude

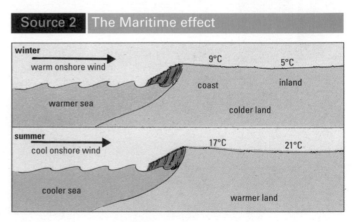

Source 2 | The Maritime effect

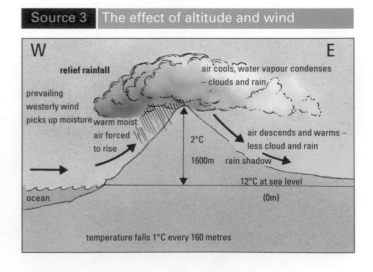

Source 3 | The effect of altitude and wind

Air masses

Air masses are large bodies of air in the atmosphere. The area where they form is called the **source region**. In the source region the air mass remains stationary for a long time and picks up the temperature and moisture characteristics of the area.

Source 4 shows the main air masses which affect the UK. The tropical maritime air mass, for example, has its source over the sea in the tropics, so the air mass is warm and moist. Warm air can hold more moisture than cold air. Air masses move away from their source region and affect the weather in the area they invade.

Anticyclones and depressions

The atmosphere pushes down on the earth's surface causing pressure. Warm air tends to rise and form **low pressure**. Cold, heavy air tends to sink and form **high pressure** (Source 5). Areas of low pressure are called **depressions**. Areas of high pressure are called **anticyclones**. A ridge of high pressure sometimes forms between two depressions, or a trough of low pressure between two anticyclones.

On a **synoptic chart** (weather map) pressure is shown by **isobars**. These are lines joining places with the same pressure. Anticyclones and depressions greatly influence the UK's weather and climate (Source 6).

Source 4	Air masses affecting the UK

Polar maritime air mass
Source: Arctic Ocean
Mild and wet in summer; cold and wet (sleet/snow) in winter

Polar air masses come from the north and are cold.

Polar continental air mass
Source: Siberia (land)
Warm and dry in summer, very cold and possibly snow in winter

Maritime air masses form over oceans so they pick up moisture and often bring rain.

Continental air masses form over land so they are drier.

Tropical maritime air mass
Source: Azores (sea)
Warm and wet in summer and mild and wet in winter

Tropical air masses come from the south and are much warmer.

Tropical continental air mass
Source: North Africa (land)
Hot and dry in summer and mild and dry in winter

Source 5	Low pressure and high pressure

high in the atmosphere

air sinking

air rising and cooling

high pressure

low pressure

air moves from high pressure to low pressure

ground surface

Source 6	Anticyclones and depressions and the UK's weather

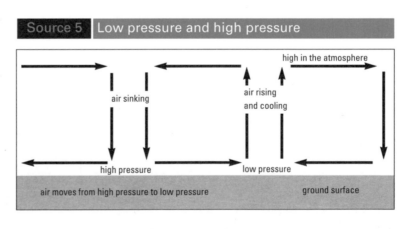

Anticyclones
There is only one air mass and so there are no fronts. Winds are light so the isobars are wide apart. Anticyclones bring stable, calm weather. In the UK they cause heatwaves in summer and cold frosty days in winter.

high pressure
1012
1008
1004

cold sector
polar air mass

low pressure

1000
996
988
986

warm sector
tropical air mass

cold front

warm front

Depressions
In a depression the pressure is lowest at the centre. Warm and cold fronts separate two air masses. In the warm sector the air mass is tropical maritime, and in the cold sector it is polar maritime. Winds blow anticlockwise towards the centre of the low pressure. Depressions bring unsettled weather with cloud and rain.

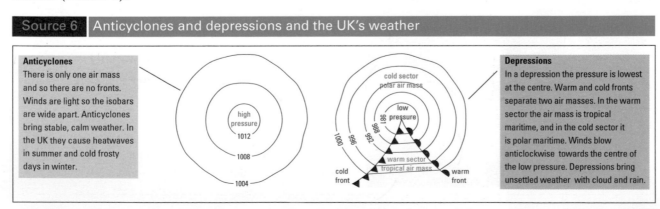

World climates

The world can be divided into climatic regions or zones. Each region has its own temperature and rainfall pattern. The map in Source 1 shows three climate zones and some climate graphs showing temperature and rainfall. In the cold climates it may not be rain which falls but snow. The word **precipitation** is used for any moisture which reaches the ground, for example snow, rain, sleet, frost.

Near the Equator the climate is hot and wet. Further north and south the climates are still hot but much drier. This is where the world's great deserts are found. Further away from the tropics, temperatures become cooler. Close to the poles the land is permanently covered with snow and ice.

The **wettest regions** in the world are:
- equatorial, which means close to the Equator, for example the Amazon Basin in South America
- monsoon regions, for example India, Bangladesh
- coasts facing onshore westerly winds, such as the west coast of Britain.

The **driest regions** in the world are:
- the interiors of Asia and North America
- the hot deserts, for example Sahara, Kalahari, Atacama
- the cold deserts, for example the Arctic and Antarctica.

| Source 1 | Three climate zones of the world |

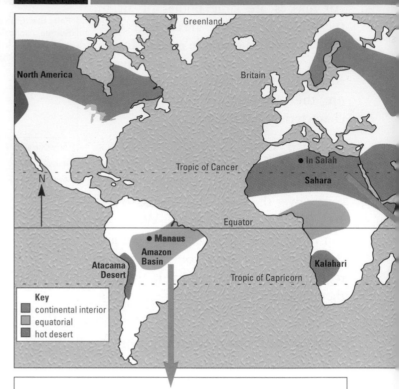

Key
- continental interior
- equatorial
- hot desert

Equatorial climate
e.g. Manaus in the Amazon Basin

Features
- hot temperatures all year: 26°C
  low temperature range: 3°C
- high annual rainfall, evenly distributed: 2000 mm per year
- no seasons
- heavy rain with thunder and lightning in the afternoons
- high humidity: 80% +

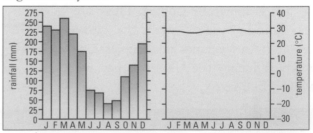

Reasons
This zone is very close to the Equator so the sun is nearly always directly overhead. It is an area of low pressure. The sun heats the ground surface. The hot air above rises and cools. The moisture in the air condenses, forming tall thunderclouds called **cumulo-nimbus**. There is heavy **convectional rainfall** often with thunder and lightning.

Siberia

Asia
● Irkutsk

India

Cold continental interior climate

e.g. Irkutsk in eastern Siberia

Features

- winter temperatures: up to - 40°C
- summer temperatures: +20°C
- large annual range of temperature: often over 55°C
- total rainfall quite low: about 400 mm per annum
- winter precipitation falls as snow

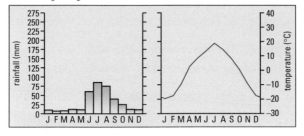

Reasons

Summer rainfall is convectional with thunderstorms caused by the land heating up and warming the air above. The hot air rises and cools. Moisture in the air condenses forming clouds and rainfall. The total rainfall is low because the area is dominated by high pressure. The high pressure brings clear skies so summer temperatures are very high. Temperatures are cooler than in the hot deserts because of the effect of latitude – this zone is further away from the Equator. In the winter, temperatures are very low. The clear skies and long nights mean a lot of heat is lost by radiation. During the day the sun is so low in the sky that temperatures remain cold.

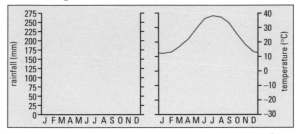

Tropical desert climate

e.g. In Salah in the Sahara desert

Features

- rain is rare: less than 120 mm per year
- temperatures vary from 29°C in hot season to 10°C in cool season
- daytime temperatures may go over 38°C but fall to 5°C at night

Reasons

The hot deserts lie in an area of high pressure. Here the air sinks and warms. Warm, sinking air rarely produces rainfall. The **trade winds** which blow in most desert areas have blown over land so are dry. The lack of cloud cover means that temperatures are very high during the day, but there is maximum heat loss by **radiation** at night.

Weather and climate
the United Kingdom

The UK weather is very variable. Colder, wetter weather is expected in the winter, and warmer, drier weather in the summer. But different parts of the country have slightly different climates. Sources 1 and 2 show rainfall and temperature patterns across the UK. The rainfall map (Source 1) shows that:

- places in the west receive more rainfall than those in the east
- upland areas are wetter than lowland areas.

The west coast of the UK lies in the path of the **prevailing** westerly winds and approaching depressions. Reaching the west coast first, far more rain falls in these areas. The upland areas are also mostly in the north and west of the UK so **relief rainfall** adds to the total. Some areas receive over 2000 mm of rain in a year. To the east, rainfall totals are generally below 650 mm. These areas are in the rain shadow of the uplands to the west. Newcastle, for example, lies in the **rain shadow** of the Pennines.

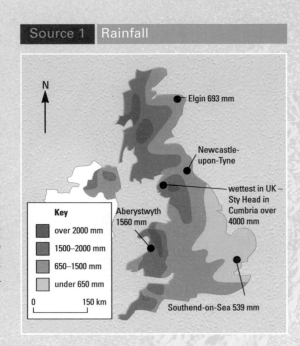

Source 1 Rainfall

Key
- over 2000 mm
- 1500–2000 mm
- 650–1500 mm
- under 650 mm

0   150 km

Elgin 693 mm
Newcastle-upon-Tyne
wettest in UK – Sty Head in Cumbria over 4000 mm
Aberystwyth 1560 mm
Southend-on-Sea 539 mm

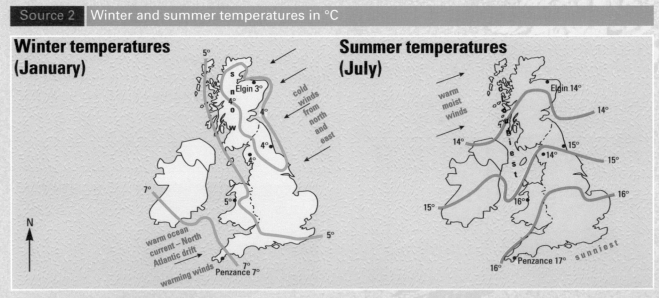

Source 2 Winter and summer temperatures in °C

Winter temperatures (January)
Elgin 3°
cold winds from north and east
warm ocean current – North Atlantic drift
warming winds Penzance 7°

Summer temperatures (July)
warm moist winds
Elgin 14°
Penzance 17° sunniest

The maps in Source 2 show that:

- in summer, the north is colder than the south
- in winter, the west coast is warmer than the east coast.

In summer, the south of the UK is warmer than the north because it is closer to the Equator and receives more **solar radiation**. In winter, the sun is very low in the sky over the UK. Solar radiation is weak and **ocean currents** have greater effect on the temperatures. The warm North Atlantic drift raises temperatures along the west coast. Cold winds from the north and east lower east-coast temperatures in winter. The Scottish Highlands receive heavy winter snowfall. Temperatures are often below freezing point because of the altitude and snow falls rather than rain.

Depressions

Depressions affect the weather in the UK for much of the year. They are areas of **low pressure** which bring cloud, rain and wind. They form over the Atlantic Ocean where warm tropical air meets cold polar air. The two types of air do not mix and where they meet is called a **front.**

By the time a depression reaches the UK it has a warm and cold front. At the fronts the warm air is forced to rise. The rising air cools, and the moisture condenses forming cloud and rainfall. Source 3 shows a synoptic chart of a series of fronts over the UK.

A typical sequence of weather takes place when a depression passes over the UK (Source 4). As the warm front approaches, wispy cirrus clouds appear high in the sky. Gradually the clouds become lower and thicker leading to steady rainfall. As the warm front passes, the temperature rises. Winds change direction to south-westerly. At the cold front the air is rising quickly and steeply. Tall cumulus and cumulo-nimbus clouds form and they bring a shorter period of heavy rainfall. There may even be hail and thunder. As the cold front passes, the temperature falls and the pressure starts to rise. Winds change direction to the north-west and conditions become brighter and drier. Depressions move from west to east and take between one and three days to pass over the UK.

Anticyclones

Anticyclones bring much more settled weather to the UK. They are areas of **high pressure** in which air is sinking. As the air descends it warms and it can hold more moisture. An anticyclone is usually accompanied by clear skies which give very warm temperatures in summer and very cold temperatures in winter. During the night the clear skies allow heat from the ground to radiate back into the atmosphere. The ground becomes much cooler and air which is in contact with the ground cools and moisture condenses. If the temperatures are below 0°C frost forms and if they are above 0°C dew forms. Water particles suspended in the air form mist and fog.

Source 3	Synoptic chart and satellite photo

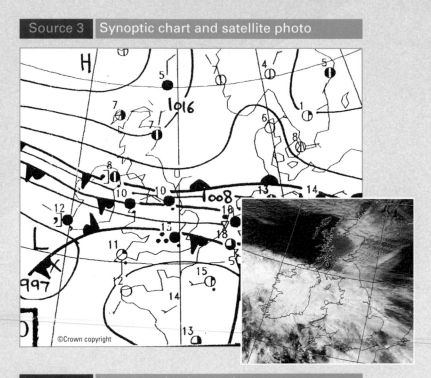

©Crown copyright

Source 4	Passage of a depression

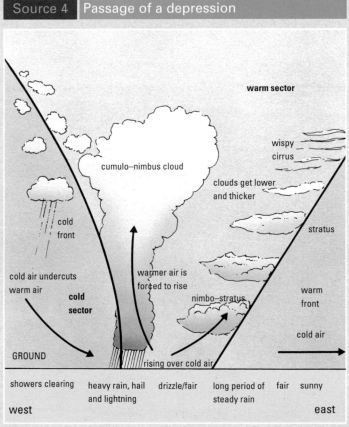

Climatic hazards
tropical storm Gordon

Tropical **cyclones** are very violent storms. The storms are accompanied by very strong winds and heavy rainfall and can be very destructive. Source 1 is a satellite photograph showing the swirling mass of cloud.

How do cyclones form?

Tropical cyclones form over the oceans where water temperatures are above 27°C. The air becomes moist and warm. Warm parcels of air rise very rapidly; the air around spirals inwards and upwards (Source 2). The air cools as it rises and the moisture condenses to form clouds and very heavy rainfall. The centre of the storm, called the 'eye', is calm. When a **hurricane** passes at first it is very stormy, followed by a short period of calm weather when the eye is overhead and then the storm begins again. Once on the land it is starved of its energy supply and it 'fizzles out'.

Tropical storm Gordon

Tropical storm Gordon left a trail of destruction in Cuba, Jamaica, Haiti and Florida in November 1994. The storm was not quite a hurricane as wind speeds were just below 120 km/hour. However, the effects were just as devastating. During the storm, 500 people were killed and the damage to homes, industry and crops ran into millions of pounds.

Modern remote sensing and satellite images can help to predict the track of a tropical storm. Local communities are warned of the storm's arrival by broadcasts on the TV and radio. But there is still enormous damage. People are drowned, or killed by falling trees and buildings. Crops are destroyed and animals killed. Power lines collapse and communications are disrupted. There are often landslides and the

| Source 1 | Satellite view of a tropical cyclone |

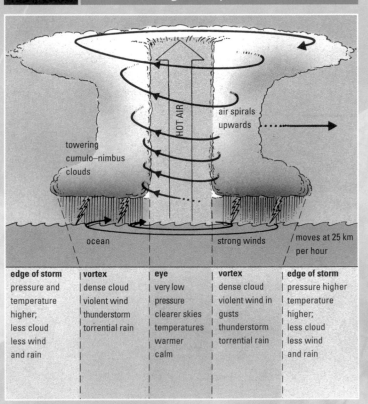

| Source 2 | Section through a tropical storm |

edge of storm	vortex	eye	vortex	edge of storm
pressure and temperature higher; less cloud less wind and rain	dense cloud violent wind thunderstorm torrential rain	very low pressure clearer skies temperatures warmer calm	dense cloud violent wind in gusts thunderstorm torrential rain	pressure higher temperature higher; less cloud less wind and rain

fast-flowing water erodes the soil, carving huge gulleys on hillsides.

The storm can whip up huge **tidal waves** sometimes over 25 metres high. These crash against the coastline destroying coastal villages. In 1970 in Bangladesh 250 000 people were drowned by hurricane storm waves.

Source 1 — London heat island

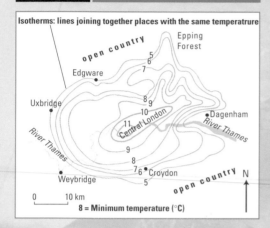

Isotherms: lines joining together places with the same temperatrure

open country

Epping Forest

Edgware

Uxbridge

Dagenham

River Thames

Central London

River Thames

Weybridge

Croydon

open country

N

0   10 km

8 = Minimum temperature (°C)

A large urban area like London, with its housing, industry, vehicles and people, creates its own **urban climate** which is different to the rural areas which surround it.

The urban heat island

The urban area tends to be a few degrees warmer than the surrounding area. This is called the **urban heat island** effect. The materials from which the roads and buildings have been made absorb heat during the day and, like a giant storage heater, release it at night. Factories, homes, offices and cars also release large amounts of heat. Source 1 shows that the inner area of London was over 6°C warmer than the surroundings on one day in May.

Source 2 — London's microclimate

Wind speeds are lower in urban areas because of friction with the buildings, but in the centre of London and other large cities the very tall skyscrapers create 'canyons' along which the wind funnels.

London is cloudier than the rural areas nearby.

Raindrops form around small dust particles so urban areas may have higher rainfall.

Urban areas like London receive less snowfall. Any snow melts quickly on the warmer streets.

Water vapour is released by burning fossil fuels, from cooling towers and from water surfaces like lakes.

There is more runoff in cities because of the impermeable surfaces, e.g. the tarmac and concrete. There is also less evapo-transpiration because there are fewer green areas.

The warmer atmosphere in the urban area causes convection. The rising warm air cools, and condenses, leading to heavy rainfall.

World soils

Covering most of the world's land surface is a thin layer of soil. Soils contain five main ingredients (Source 1). These are:

- mineral particles from the breakdown or weathering of rocks
- humus – decayed plant and animal remains
- water – in the spaces between soil particles
- air – in the pore spaces
- living organisms – earthworms, bacteria.

Within a soil the amount of each of these ingredients varies. Soils are also formed on different rock types, in different climates and below different vegetation. Source 1 shows that there are many different soil types.

Source 1 Selected world soils

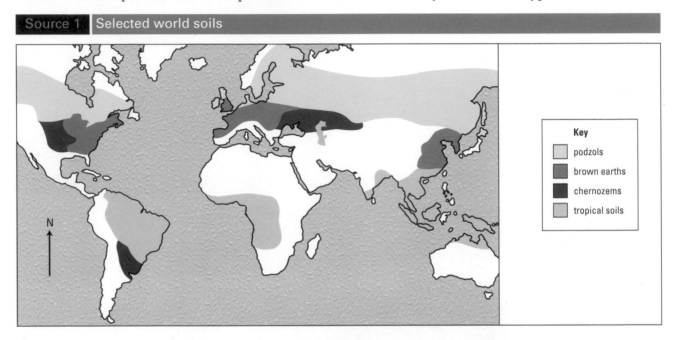

Key
- podzols
- brown earths
- chernozems
- tropical soils

The soil profile

In order to study different types of soil a **soil profile** can be drawn. A soil profile is a section which looks at the soil from the earth's surface to the bedrock below. Most profiles have three layers which are called **horizons.** The horizons are lettered A, B and C in Source 2.

Source 2 Soil profile

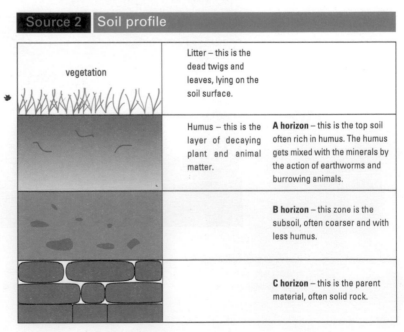

vegetation

Litter – this is the dead twigs and leaves, lying on the soil surface.

Humus – this is the layer of decaying plant and animal matter.

A horizon – this is the top soil often rich in humus. The humus gets mixed with the minerals by the action of earthworms and burrowing animals.

B horizon – this zone is the subsoil, often coarser and with less humus.

C horizon – this is the parent material, often solid rock.

World soil types

Climate is the most important factor in soil formation and each major soil type matches up with a climate type. These major soil types are called 'zonal soils'. Study the information in Source 3 to find out more about three of the world's zonal soils.

| Source 3 | Three zonal soils |

Brown earths, e.g. lowland UK

Horizons

A – Rich mixture of humus and minerals
   Dark brown, crumb structure
B – Mineral horizon with some humus
C – Bedrock

deciduous forest
neutral pH (5–6.5)
moderate rainfall

How is it formed?

Grasses and deciduous trees add a lot of humus. This is well mixed by earthworms.
The A and B horizons merge into one another. There is no clear boundary because of the mixing by animals and the small amount of leaching. Little clay, iron or humus is washed down.

Podzols, e.g. central USA, Russia, uplands in the UK

Horizons

A – Thin black layer of humus on top of light-coloured topsoil
B – Red subsoil with black staining
C – Bedrock usually acid

grasslands
acid pH = 4.0
heavy rainfall

How is it formed?

The surface layer is peaty. Plant remains do not rot away well because it is cold and wet and acid. The light layer has had the iron and aluminium removed by strong leaching (iron gives soil its brown colour) called podzolisation. There is a sharp change into the B horizon where the iron has been redeposited giving it its red colour. Sometimes the iron is deposited in a thin layer at the top of the B horizon. This is an iron pan.

Chernozems, e.g. continental interiors

Horizons

A – Thick layer up to 1 metre. Black, crumb structure. Grades slowly into light-coloured zone. Notice the animal burrows (dark patches)
C – Rich loëss parent material
 – fine, wind blown and silty, high in calcium (white patches)

grasslands
neutral pH)
light rainfall

How is it formed?

A large amount of humus from grass stems and roots.
Very dark humus in A horizon, well mixed by earthworm activity.
No B horizon. A horizon lies on top of C horizon, which is very rich in nodules of calcium. The dry summers and cold winters restrict the rotting of the humus. Rainfall is light but evaporation high so in summer water moves upwards through the profile causing calcification – the calcium is concentrated in the C horizon.

Ecosystems

Studying ecosystems is a good way to investigate the environment because they involve climate, soils, vegetation, animals and human activities. Source 1 shows a natural ecosystem. There are living organisms, such as the trees and animals, and non-living elements, such as the soil and climate. The elements in an ecosystem are linked together by a cycling of water, energy and nutrients.

Ecosystems are very fragile. Many ecosystems are being damaged by human activity. Today, there is very little of the world's natural vegetation left as people have cleared large areas for housing, farming, industry and communications.

Source 1 | A natural ecosystem

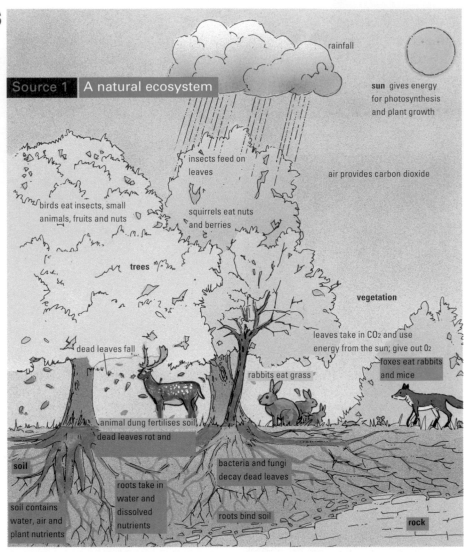

rainfall

sun gives energy for photosynthesis and plant growth

insects feed on leaves

air provides carbon dioxide

birds eat insects, small animals, fruits and nuts

squirrels eat nuts and berries

trees

vegetation

leaves take in CO$_2$ and use energy from the sun; give out O$_2$

dead leaves fall

foxes eat rabbits and mice

rabbits eat grass

animal dung fertilises soil

dead leaves rot and

soil

bacteria and fungi decay dead leaves

roots take in water and dissolved nutrients

soil contains water, air and plant nutrients

roots bind soil

rock

Source 2 | World vegetation zones

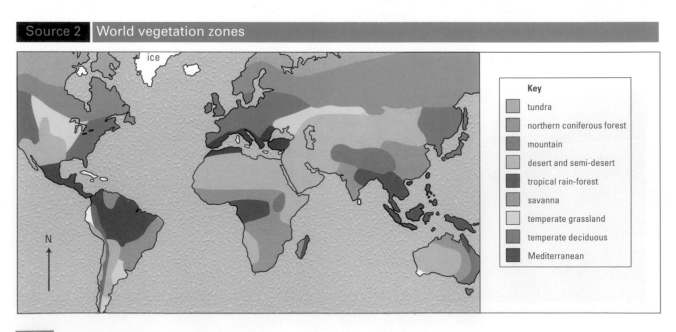

ice

Key

- tundra
- northern coniferous forest
- mountain
- desert and semi-desert
- tropical rain-forest
- savanna
- temperate grassland
- temperate deciduous
- Mediterranean

N

Biomes

There are several types of ecosystem which are named after the main vegetation, for example: deciduous forest, tropical rainforest and grassland. Source 2 shows the distribution of world vegetation types. They are similar to the world climate and soil zones. These vegetation, soil and climate zones are called **biomes.**

Ecosystems can also be studied at a smaller scale, for example a pond, an oak wood or a hedgerow. This is useful because there are many small-scale variations in vegetation caused by slight changes in the climate or soil.

The coniferous forest ecosystem

Coniferous forests are sometimes called Boreal forests or taiga. They are mostly found in high latitudes across northern Europe and Asia and across northern North America (Source 2). These zones have cold climates with winter temperatures of below −20°C and only short summers up to +15°C. Precipitation totals are low, about 300 millimetres per year with most falling in the summer.

Most of the trees are **evergreen** conifers like those in Source 3. Some examples are spruce, pine and fir. The forests tend to be in single stands. This means they are all of one tree type.

The forests mostly grow in areas with **podzol** soils. The pine needles from the trees provide little humus. They rot very slowly because it is so cold. Although the rainfall is low there is very little evaporation, so most of the moisture can travel down through the soil causing leaching. Source 3 shows how the coniferous forests are well adapted to the long, cold, snowy winters.

| Source 3 | Coniferous forest ecosystem |

conical shape and flexible branches to allow snow to slide off

only one layer of vegetation

needles not leaves to reduce water loss by transpiration

evergreen (keeps leaves all year) – can begin to photosynthesise as soon as it is warm enough (short growing season)

thick bark and tough thick needles to protect from cold

shallow roots to collect water

subsoil frozen

little undergrowth – frozen ground and little light

podzol soils

carpet of pine needles

A grassland ecosystem
North America's prairies

The temperate grasslands of North America are known as the **prairies**. They cover a huge area stretching from the Great Lakes in the east to the Rocky mountains in the west (Source 1). Large parts of the prairies are level and low lying. Most of the land in the east is less than 300 metres above sea level. The soils are deep, fertile chernozems (see page 83).

(see page 83)

Source 1	The Prairie Provinces, Canada

Hudson Bay

Alberta

Manitoba

Edmonton

Rocky Mountains

Saskatoon

Calgary Saskatchewan

Regina Winnipeg

N

0   500 km

Source 2	The natural landscape of the prairies

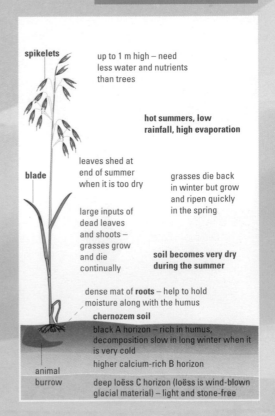

The area has a continental interior climate. Rainfall decreases from east to west but on average it is about 400 millimetres. Most of the rain falls in summer as convectional rainfall. Winter precipitation falls as snow. In the winter temperatures are as low as -20°C. High winds can cause blizzards. The soil is frozen for several months of the year.

In the spring, the warm 'chinook' wind comes from the west and can raise the temperature from -20°C to above 0°C in a few minutes. The snow melts and spring comes quickly! Summer temperatures rise to 20°C. The heating causes convectional rainfall and hailstorms.

The climate is too dry for trees to grow. Instead:

- the landscape is covered by tall prairie grasses with occasional trees along water courses (Source 2)
- the grasses are well adapted to the short growing season and the dry conditions (Source 3)
- the grasses are dormant in the winter but grow rapidly in spring and summer
- towards the Rocky mountains, where it is drier, the grasses become shorter and more tussocky.

The prairies have excellent fertile soil, flat land and some summer rainfall. This makes them attractive to farmers for wheat growing. However, the farmers also have to cope with winter blizzards, summer drought, hailstorms, soil erosion and tornadoes.

Source 3	How the grasses adapt to the climate

spikelets

up to 1 m high – need less water and nutrients than trees

hot summers, low rainfall, high evaporation

blade

leaves shed at end of summer when it is too dry

grasses die back in winter but grow and ripen quickly in the spring

large inputs of dead leaves and shoots – grasses grow and die continually

soil becomes very dry during the summer

dense mat of **roots** – help to hold moisture along with the humus

chernozem soil

black A horizon – rich in humus, decomposition slow in long winter when it is very cold

higher calcium-rich B horizon

animal burrow

deep loëss C horizon (loëss is wind-blown glacial material) – light and stone-free

Source 1 — Location of the Sahel

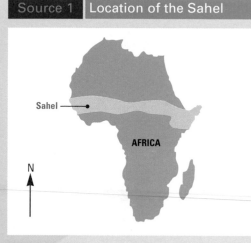

Sahel

AFRICA

N

The Sahel is a narrow belt of land in North Africa. It borders the southern edge of the Sahara desert (Source 1).

The climate is semi-desert. Temperatures are always warm and there is a long dry season (Source 2). There is just enough rainfall for grasses and some drought resistant shrubs and trees (Source 3).

In some years there is less rainfall, fewer grasses grow and trees may die. The landscape becomes much more like desert (Source 4). This climate change is one cause of **desertification**. Desertification is also speeded up by human activity. Up until the 1960s there was more rainfall in the Sahel and the population grew. Water was plentiful so more crops were grown and numbers of animals increased. Wood was available to use as fuel and building materials.

In the drier years after the 1960s large areas of forest were removed for farmland and fuel supplies. People still tried to grow the same crops and rear the same numbers of animals. **Overgrazing** and **overcultivation** left the ground bare. Without vegetation less humus is added to the soil. The soil holds less water and dries out. The bare soil is quickly eroded by wind and flash floods. The land can no longer support any trees and plants and it turns to desert. Since 1970:

- there has been widespread crop failure
- over 100 000 people and millions of animals have died.

A variety of techniques can be used to prevent desertification and also to rehabilitate the land that has already been damaged. New research using satellite images suggests that the deserts may not be spreading permanently. Some areas where rainfall has increased have now recovered. It is also difficult to decide whether it is the climate or the human activity which causes the changes. One thing is certain – the semi-arid lands are fragile environments and people must use them with care so that desertification is avoided.

Source 2 — Climate graph of the Sahel

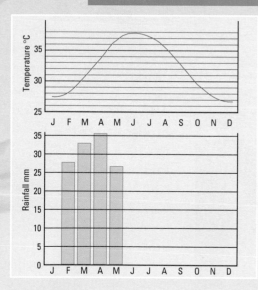

Source 3 — The Sahel before desertification

Source 4 — The Sahel after desertification

How vegetation adapts
tropical rainforest in Brazil

Brazil is the largest country in South America. In the north, the climate is equatorial (page 76). The hot, wet greenhouse conditions produce very rapid growth of vegetation all year round. The tropical rainforest is the richest vegetation in the world. Study Source 1 and notice the five layers of vegetation and the large variety of different trees and plants. There are over 1000 different tree species, for example mahogany, teak and rosewood. Study Sources 2 and 3 to discover how very well adapted the vegetation is to the special conditions in the rainforest.

Source 1	Tropical rainforest

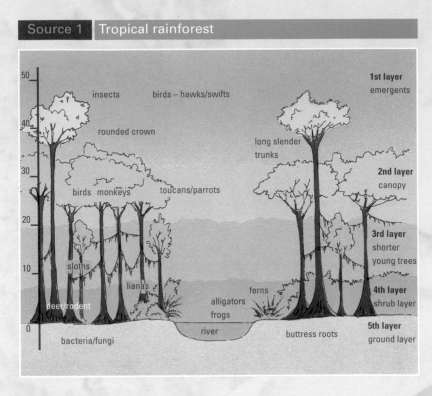

Source 2	Buttress roots

The huge buttress roots at the base of the trees help to give the trees support and to take in the vast quantities of water and nutrients the trees need to survive.

Source 3	Drip tips

Some of the leaves have drip tips which act like the lip on a jug helping the leaves to shed water. This stops disease.

A fragile environment

The lush rainforest vegetation fools people into thinking the soils are fertile. But these tropical soils are infertile and heavy rainfall quickly leaches the minerals. About 90 per cent of all the nutrients in the rainforest are held in the trees. Cutting down the trees removes the nutrients and leaves the soil unprotected. The tropical rainforest ecosystem is very fragile and easily damaged.

the Jengka Triangle Project, Malaysia

Deforestation is a major world problem. Many governments have encouraged the clearing of the rainforests because:

- the revenue earned from selling timber, drugs and minerals helps to pay off debts and to develop their countries
- new land is needed to house and feed the growing population in countries like Brazil and Malaysia.

In Malaysia the FELDA (Federal Land Development Authority) has cleared forest to allow 307 projects to set up plantations to grow rubber and oil palm. The Jengka Triangle Project is one example which aimed to develop 40 500 hectares of oil palm and rubber and to house 9000 families. The total area for the scheme is 121 406 hectares of mainly tropical rainforest (Source 1).

Before the scheme began, sawmills, wood processing factories and roads were built to process the cut timber. The trees were cut using modern machines such as chainsaws and cranes (Source 2). The logs were moved by huge tractors and lorries. The less valuable trees and plants were burnt. Rubber and oil palm were planted and settlements built. The finished scheme has a good network of roads, processing factories for the oil palm and rubber, timber and plywood factories and three new towns.

Today, there are many large-scale projects like the Jengka Triangle Project, and the scale of forest removal is huge. Source 3 shows some of the problems caused by the deforestation.

Source 2   Jengka Triangle Project

Source 3   Problems caused by forest removal

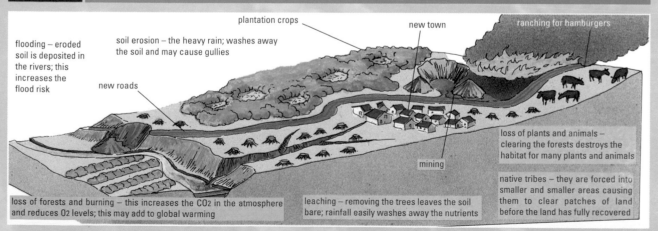

flooding – eroded soil is deposited in the rivers; this increases the flood risk

soil erosion – the heavy rain; washes away the soil and may cause gullies

plantation crops

new town

ranching for hamburgers

new roads

loss of plants and animals – clearing the forests destroys the habitat for many plants and animals

mining

native tribes – they are forced into smaller and smaller areas causing them to clear patches of land before the land has fully recovered

loss of forests and burning – this increases the CO_2 in the atmosphere and reduces O_2 levels; this may add to global warming

leaching – removing the trees leaves the soil bare; rainfall easily washes away the nutrients

1 Study the photograph on page 71. Are the following statements true or false? Try to explain each of your answers.

   a There is a lot of cloud over the Sahara desert.

   b There is a lot of cloud approaching the UK.

   c There is a lot of cloud over the equatorial area of West Africa.

2 a Name five elements of the weather.

   b Draw labelled sketches of the instruments used to measure temperature, rainfall, sunshine, humidity and pressure.

   c Write notes alongside each one to explain how it works.

   d Explain why you would not site a weather station close to some tall trees and buildings.

3 Complete a table like the one below to give the features of air masses affecting the UK. The table has been started for you.

Air mass	polar continental			tropical maritime	
Source region		North Africa			Arctic Ocean
Summer weather					
Winter weather					

4 a On a world map mark and label three climate zones.

   b Using the figures in Source 1 draw a climate graph.

Source 1 Climate figures

Months	J	F	M	A	M	J	J	A	S	O	N	D
Temp °C	20	21	26	32	38	39	39	35	30	23	20	18
Rain fall mm	0	20	30	35	18	0	0	0	0	0	0	0

   c Describe the main features of the climate graph you have drawn. Include the maximum and minimum temperatures, the range of temperature, the rainfall total and any dry or wet seasons.

   d Using the information on pages 76–7 decide what type of climate you have described.

5 a Copy and complete the paragraph below.

Scotland and the north of England are *(colder/warmer)* than the south of England in summer. This is because the south is *(further from/closer to)* the Equator. In winter, the east coast is *(colder/warmer)* than the west coast. This is because there are *(cold/warm)* winds from the north and east. Also the west coast is affected by the *(warm/cold)* ocean currents. The north and west of the UK receive *(more/less)* rainfall than the south and east. This is because the warm *(moist/dry)* winds come in from the west. The uplands are *(colder/warmer)* than lowlands and receive *(more/less)* rain. This is because temperatures *(decrease/increase)* with height and there is relief rainfall.

   b Copy the diagrams and labels from page 74 to explain the effect of latitude, prevailing winds and altitude.

6 Choose one of the following ecosystems: coniferous forest; tropical rainforest; temperate grassland.

    a Mark and label its distribution on a world map.

    b Describe the climate and soils of the region.

    c Describe the features of the vegetation.

    d Explain how the vegetation is adapted to the climate.

7 a Describe the Jengka Triangle Project as an example of deforestation.

    b Divide your class into four to represent one of the following groups of people:

- the Malaysian government
- a shifting cultivator
- an international logging company
- a conservation group like Greenpeace.

In your chosen role write a report in favour of or against the development of the rainforest. Present your report to the class as a whole.

Following your presentations decide which groups were in favour of conservation or development.

    c In your groups study Source 2 and write a definition for sustainable development based on the role that you have chosen.

Source 2   **What is sustainable development?**

Today, people are supporting the idea of sustainable development. This is the ability of one generation to hand over to the next at least the same amount of resources it started with. It should also be development which helps all people, particularly the poorest. Sustainable development should:

- respect the environment and cultures
- use traditional skills and knowledge
- give people control over their land and lives
- use appropriate technology – machines and equipment that are cheap, easy to use and do not harm the environment
- generate income for communities.

---

    d Look again at the Jengka Triangle Project. Write two lists, one for the ways in which the project supports sustainable development and one for the ways in which it does not.

    e Try to produce some suggestions for the Malaysian government as to how it could improve it's development projects in the future.

8 a Draw a sketch map to show the location of the Sahel.

    b Study the photographs (Sources 3 and 4) on page 87. Describe and explain the changes which have taken place.

1 Weather

The weather is the state of the atmosphere at one time. Weather instruments are used to measure temperature, rainfall, wind speed and direction. These instruments need to be carefully sited. The maximum and minimum thermometers and the wet and dry bulb thermometer are kept in a Stevenson screen. The station also has a sunshine recorder, a rain gauge, a wind vane and an anemometer. The barometer used to measure pressure may be indoors.

2 Climate

Climate is the average weather of an area calculated from many years of weather records. The climate changes from place to place. For example, places near the Equator have hot, wet equatorial climates and the tropical deserts have hot, dry climates. The UK has a west-coast maritime climate but there are also small differences in the climate across different parts of the country. Many factors affect climate, including: latitude, altitude, prevailing winds, aspect and the maritime effect.

3 Climatic hazards

Some parts of the world are affected by climatic hazards such as drought in the Sahel, tropical storms in the Caribbean, hailstorms and tornadoes in the prairies. Tropical storms are very destructive, bringing strong winds and torrential rain.

4 Microclimates

Buildings and vegetation can create their own small-scale climate called a microclimate. London, for example, has its own urban microclimate. The concentration of housing, offices, industries and vehicles has affected:
- temperature which is usually higher than the rural areas,
- cloud and rainfall which are greater
- wind speeds which are on average lower than the rural areas although they may be higher if the air is funnelled down the 'canyons' created by the skyscrapers.

5 Soils

Soils contain mineral particles, humus, water, air and living organisms. There are many different types of soils in the world. Three examples are podzols, brown earths and chernozems. A soil profile is drawn to show the characteristics of a soil. Different layers or horizons can be recognised called the A, B and C horizons.

6 Ecosystems

Ecosystems allow a whole environment to be studied including the climate, soils, vegetation and animals. In an ecosystem there are stores and flows of energy and nutrients. Biomes are large–scale ecosystems named after the main type of vegetation, for example the tropical rainforest and grasslands.

The vegetation in an ecosystem shows many adaptations to the climate in which it grows. Trees in the rainforest are adapted to the hot, wet greenhouse conditions; grasses in the prairies are adapted to very cold winters and hot summers.

There is very little natural vegetation left in the world today. The natural vegetation which remains is also under threat. The coniferous forests of North America and Europe are being felled for paper and furniture.The tropical rainforests are being cleared for a variety of development projects and semi-desert areas like the Sahel are threatened by desertification.

Population

People galore

Distribution and density

There are more than five billion people living in the world today. They are unevenly spread across the earth's surface.

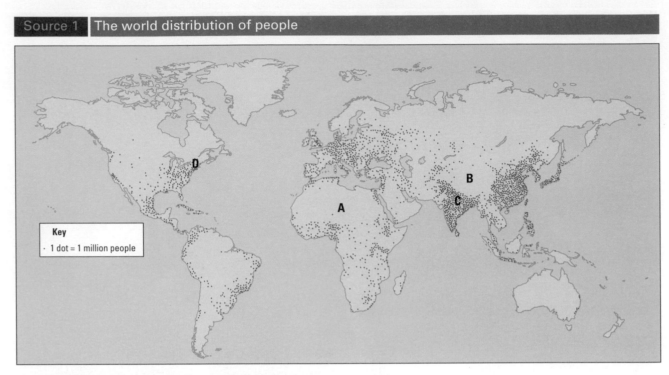

Key
· 1 dot = 1 million people

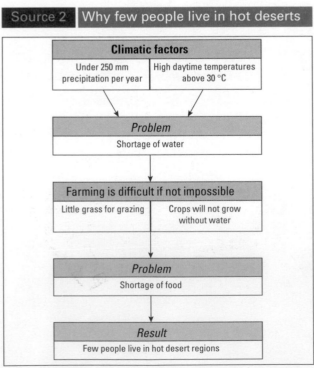

Climatic factors	
Under 250 mm precipitation per year	High daytime temperatures above 30 °C

Problem
Shortage of water

Farming is difficult if not impossible	
Little grass for grazing	Crops will not grow without water

Problem
Shortage of food

Result
Few people live in hot desert regions

A dot map as in Source 1, is used to show population distribution. One dot represents 1 million people. In some areas, without the natural resources to attract settlement, there are few people. This pattern or **distribution of population** can be seen in Source 1. The main problem for people living in the area marked A is that it is too dry. It is also very hot during the day. Therefore **climate** has discouraged people from living there (Source 2).

The area marked B on Source 1 is the Himalayas. These mountains include Mount Everest, the world's highest mountain, which rises to 8848 metres above sea level. These mountains are too high and too steep for many people to make a living there. **Relief** therefore has discouraged people from living in this area.

Density of population is the number of people per square kilometre. It is worked out by using the following formula.

$$\frac{\text{number of people living in an area}}{\text{size of the area in which they live}} = \text{population density}$$

To explain why some areas of the world have high densities of population, more than one favourable factor is needed. The factors may be **physical,** such as climate, relief and soils. They may be **human,** such as economic, social and political. Source 3 shows farmers growing rice in the Ganges valley in India (marked C on Source 1). The labels on Source 3 show the favourable physical and human factors which help to explain why rural densities of population here are among the highest in the world. Different colours have been used to distinguish between the physical and human factors.

| Source 3 | Cultivating rice in the Ganges valley |

monsoon climate

hot: about 27°C

wet in summer
(above 100 mm rain)

people do the work

flat land

fertile silt soils

large amount of rice grown to feed a lot of people

irrigation water

| Source 4 | The World Trade Centre in New York |

However, most of the areas of high density of population in the world are in urban areas. Letter D on Source 1 marks the east coast of the USA centred around New York. There is an almost continuous line of cities between Boston and Washington. The great variety and number of jobs make it possible for large numbers of people to make a living there. The list of city-based jobs is almost endless. There are jobs in factories (secondary) as well as in offices, transport, shops, cafés and hotels (tertiary). Source 4 shows a well-known New York landmark, the World Trade Centre. Each tower has over 100 storeys. Over 50 000 people work in these two towers alone.

Population change

Population change may mean an increase or a decrease in the number of people living in an area. It is natural to assume that it means population increase because the world's population is continuing to grow as Source 1 shows.

Birth rates

High **birth rates** contribute to population growth. Birth rate is the number of live births per 1000 people per year in a country or region. Source 2 shows the average birth rates for the different continents. Notice how much higher the average birth rate is in Africa, where there are many less economically developed countries (LEDCs), compared with Europe, where most of the countries are more economically developed (MEDCs). Some of the factors which help to explain these differences are given in Source 3.

In general it is true to say that birth rates in the world are declining as more and more people are practising birth control. Wealth and education are the best contraceptives: richer and better educated people have fewer children. Why, therefore, is world population continuing to increase? It is necessary to look at the other element in the formula – the **death rate**.

Death rates

Low death rates contribute to population growth. Death rate is the number of deaths per 1000 people per year in a country or region. Death rates are at an all time low (Source 2). Notice how much lower the death rates are than the birth rates. The reason for this is improved medical treatment and **primary health care,** which reduces the chances of a person becoming ill in the first place. Source 4 illustrates some of the ways in which this can be done. **Secondary health care** is more widely available. Particularly in the cities in LEDCs, there are hospitals to treat sick people, where modern medicines and drugs are available.

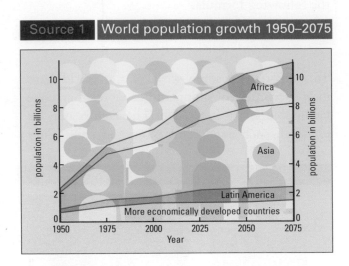

Source 1 World population growth 1950–2075

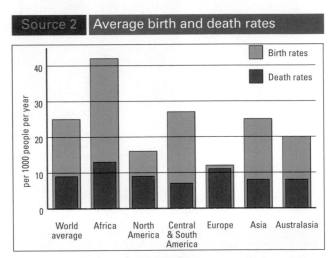

Source 2 Average birth and death rates

Source 3 Factors which affect the birth rate

Factor	High birth rates in LEDCs	Low birth rates in MEDCs
Economic	• Children can work on the farm or earn money begging or selling goods in the city. • Children support elderly parents.	• Children cost their parents a lot of money. • Pensions for the old.
Social	• Little use of birth control. • 6–10 children in a family is normal.	• Many methods of birth control are used. • 2–3 children are the norm.
Political	Governments in Muslim and Catholic countries will not always provide family planning education.	Government-financed family planning services.

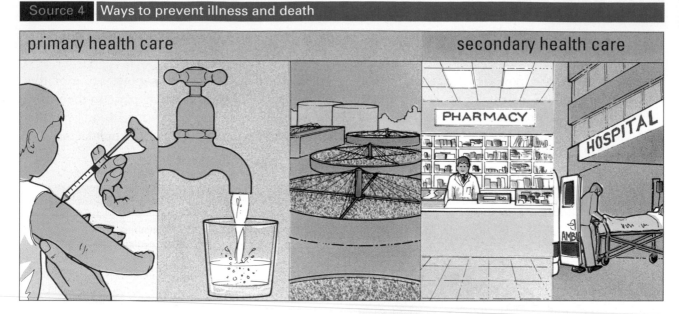

Source 4 | Ways to prevent illness and death

primary health care

secondary health care

PHARMACY

HOSPITAL

Natural increase

The rate of **natural increase** in a country or region is worked out by the following formula.

$$\frac{\text{birth rate}}{\text{death rate}} = \text{rate of natural increase}$$

Using the values from Source 2 the rates of natural increase for the continents can be worked out (Source 5).

A big difference between the birth rate and death rate, as there is for Africa (Source 5), means a high rate of natural increase and high population growth. The changing relationships between birth and death rates through time are shown on a graph called the demographic transition model (Source 6).

Source 5 | Rates of natural increase

Continent	Birth rate	Death rate	Rate of natural increase	
	per 1000	per 1000	per 1000	per 100 (%)
Europe	12	11	1	0.1
Africa	42	13	29	2.9

What has really happened is that the death rate has fallen rapidly in the LEDCs in stages 2 and 3. It has fallen much more quickly than the birth rate. The big difference between the death rate and the birth rate has resulted in the high rate of population increase. Only in the MEDCs have birth rates fallen to the same level as death rates so keeping the population increase low. Most European countries are in stage 4.

Source 6 | The demographic transition model

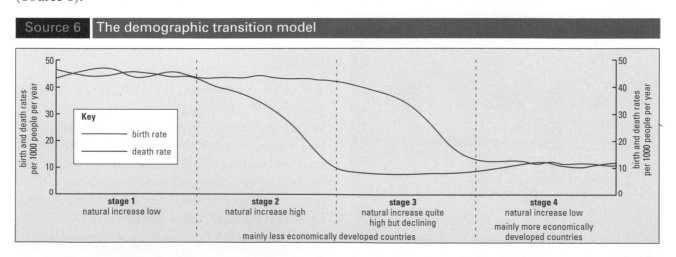

Migration

Migration means the movement of people. What makes people move? Normally there are things they do not like about where they live. These are *push* factors. Usually there are things they like about the place they are moving to. These are called *pull* factors. Source 1 shows some of the main types of migration taking place in the world today. All these types of migration can be explained by referring to push and pull factors.

Source 1   Types of migration

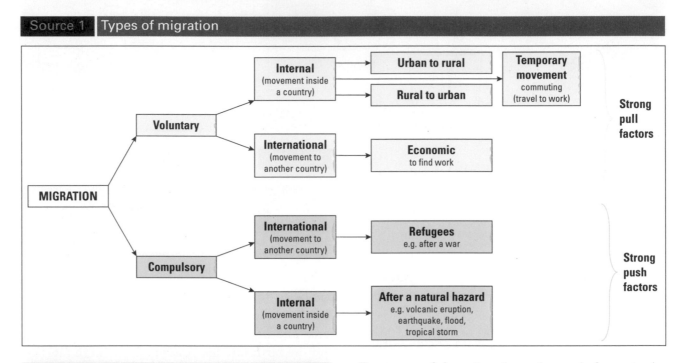

For some of the migrations the push factor is the most important. People may be forced out of a place by natural disasters or wars. They have to move whether they want to or not. They are called **refugees** if they have to flee to another country. In Peru, when a flood destroyed all the houses in a village and the farmland was covered by useless boulders (Source 2), the villagers were forced to move.

For other migrations, the pull factor is more powerful. People living in the rural areas in the world's less economically developed countries may be attracted by what they think are the chances of work and higher paid jobs in the cities. It may be the modern services that pull them towards the city: of great importance is electricity supply because they can watch the films, soaps and sport on TV – just as most people in the rich countries of the world do.

Source 2   A deserted Peruvian village

Source 3	Reasons for rural to urban migration in LEDCs

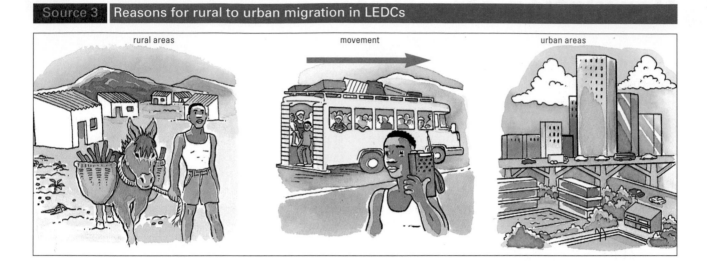

Source 4	Reasons for urban to rural migration in MEDCs

Source 3 shows the push and pull factors for **rural to urban migration,** which is the most common type of migration in LEDCs. Many people are leaving the countryside and flooding into the cities. They are making worse the already great problems in the cities but few want to go back. Life in the city is better than life in the countryside.

In contrast, in the more economically developed countries the exact opposite is happening. Some people here believe that the countryside is a better place to live than the city. Source 4 shows push and pull factors for **urban to rural migration.**

It is important to realise just how different living in the countryside is in the rich countries compared with the poor countries. In rich countries piped water and electricity exist in the countryside just as they do in the towns. Many people own cars, which means they have easy access to the shops, services and places of work in the towns.

However, there are many problems associated with both types of migration. Rural to urban migration causes population growth in the city which leads to urban problems, such as housing shortages, lack of essential services and unemployment. Urban to rural migration causes the growth of the village which leads to a change in its character. Conflicts often develop between old residents and newcomers, house prices increase and there is more traffic.

Population structure

Information about the characteristics of a population, such as age, sex and ethnic make-up, is recorded in a census. The age-sex composition of a population is known as the **population structure.** It is shown by a population pyramid. The percentage for each age group is plotted by horizontal bars for males and females. Source 1 shows the population pyramids for Zaire in Africa and the United Kingdom in Europe. Zaire is in stage 2 in the demographic transition model (see page 97) while the UK is in stage 4.

(see page 97)

Source 1	Population pyramids for Zaire and the UK

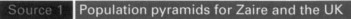
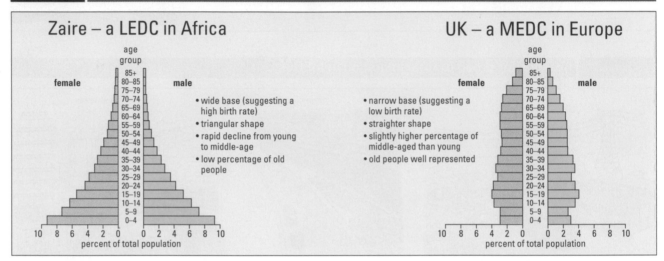

Zaire – a LEDC in Africa

female   male

- wide base (suggesting a high birth rate)
- triangular shape
- rapid decline from young to middle-age
- low percentage of old people

UK – a MEDC in Europe

female   male

- narrow base (suggesting a low birth rate)
- straighter shape
- slightly higher percentage of middle-aged than young
- old people well represented

It is possible to use the population pyramids to work out the **dependency ratio.** Those over 65 and below 15 are regarded as **dependants.** Most of them do not work and so they need to rely upon some income from those in work. The dependency ratio can be worked out from the percentage values taken from the pyramids in Source 1.

Source 2	There are plenty of young people in LEDCs

Zaire		UK	
% under 15	= 46	% under 15	= 18
% over 65	= 4	% over 65	= 15
% dependants	= 50	% dependants	= 33
Ratio dependant : worker	= 1:1	Ratio dependant : worker	= 1:2

The dependency ratio is so high in Zaire because of the large numbers of young people (Source 2).

Population problems

(i) LEDCs

It is very difficult for a poor country to provide the clean water, electricity, schools and all the other services that its young and growing population needs. Soon these young people will have families of their own. Even though many of these young people are better educated about birth control than were their parents, there are so many of them that, even with smaller families, the population will increase for many years to come. This has been described as a 'demographic time bomb'. A more basic question is, 'How is everyone going to be fed?' More food is needed from the land but can food be provided without further damage to the environment (Source 3)?

(ii) MEDCs

In countries such as the UK it is not the high dependency ratio, but the **ageing population** which is the 'demographic time bomb'. There is an increasing proportion of people over 65. For these countries one big cost is providing state pensions for an increasing number of people. Also the elderly need to use state medical services more frequently. The cost of care for the old in residential homes is already spiralling upwards (Source 4).

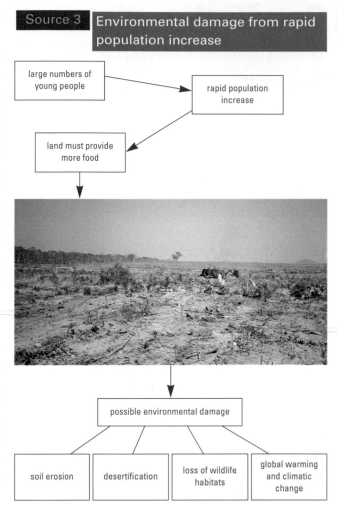

Source 3 Environmental damage from rapid population increase

large numbers of young people → rapid population increase → land must provide more food → possible environmental damage → soil erosion | desertification | loss of wildlife habitats | global warming and climatic change

Source 4 Europe's population is growing old

Elderly population

key
65+
75+
85+

millions in the UK

1901 1931 1951 1961 1971 1981 1991 2001 2011 2021 2031 2041 2051

People over 65 in selected European countries

percent

Sweden Norway UK Austria Germany Italy France Portugal Ireland

INCREASE STATE PENSIONS

IMPROVE THE HEALTH SERVICES FOR THE OLD

LOWER THE COST OF CARE IN RESIDENTIAL HOMES

Population distribution
the United Kingdom

Source 1 shows variations in population density within the United Kingdom. The map suggests an uneven spread of people across the country.

High density

Certain areas of high density can be identified. Some of the largest areas of high density are associated with the seven **conurbations** named on Source 1. Conurbations are large, continuously built-up areas around a big city or cities. The most continuous area of high population density stretches from Greater London through the Midlands to the major conurbations in northern England around Liverpool (Merseyside), Manchester (Greater Manchester) and Leeds–Bradford (West Yorkshire).

Low density

Certain areas of low density are equally clear on Source 1. The most extensive areas with low population densities are upland areas, which are mainly located in the northern and western parts of the country. Areas of intermediate population density fill the lowland areas between the big cities. Lowland areas cover more of the land area in England than they do in Wales and Scotland.

Reasons for different densities

Why do some areas have higher population densities than others? It is always necessary to refer to several factors for a full explanation (Source 2).

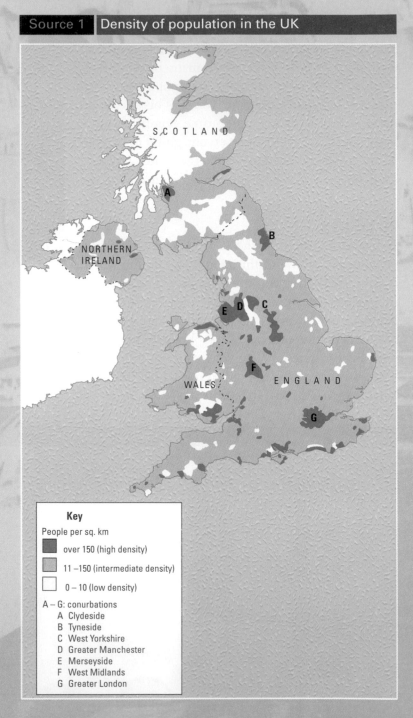

Source 1 Density of population in the UK

SCOTLAND

NORTHERN IRELAND

WALES

ENGLAND

Key

People per sq. km

■ over 150 (high density)

▨ 11 –150 (intermediate density)

□ 0 – 10 (low density)

A – G: conurbations
  A Clydeside
  B Tyneside
  C West Yorkshire
  D Greater Manchester
  E Merseyside
  F West Midlands
  G Greater London

Source 2 Reasons for different population densities

Highlands of Scotland
Reasons for the **low population density:**

Physical factors

A Climate – cool summers and high precipitation

B Relief – high land and steep slopes

C Soils – thin and acid soils and much of the land is bare rock

Economic factors

• remote position away from the markets

• poor communications with few railway lines and no motorways

Results

• there is a lot of unproductive land

• farming is difficult and cannot employ many people

• industry is not interested in locating here

Comment

This example is a reminder of the importance of physical factors for explaining low densities of population.

Greater London
Reasons for the **high population density:**

Historical factors

• the capital city with many Government departments

• long-established centre for business and trade in the City

Economic factors

It is an attractive location for industry and business because:

• of the large and wealthy market both in London and the south-east

• it is the centre for communications with fast rail services and good motorway links (such as the M1 to the North, M40 to the Midlands, M4 to South Wales)

• its position is close to Europe

Results

• no other part of the country can match the variety of work

• there is an enormous variety of jobs in the service sector – in government, in banks and offices, in transport, in shops and in serving visitors in hotels, and places of entertainment

Comment

Human advantages are concentrated here in a way not found in any other part of the UK.

East Anglia
Reasons for the **intermediate population density:**

Physical factors

A Climate – warm summers and less precipitation

B Relief – low and gently sloping land (most below 100 m above sea level)

C Soils – deep soils of various deposits such as fertile silt and boulder clay

Economic factors

• close to the London market and the most heavily populated part of the country

• access by motorway such as the M11, to London

Results

• farmers can grow many different crops but don't need too many workers because of mechanisation

• the market towns have processing plants for the farm produce

• some industries will locate here because it is near London

Comment

Physical factors are favourable for settlement. It has some economic advantages but not as many as in big cities such as London.

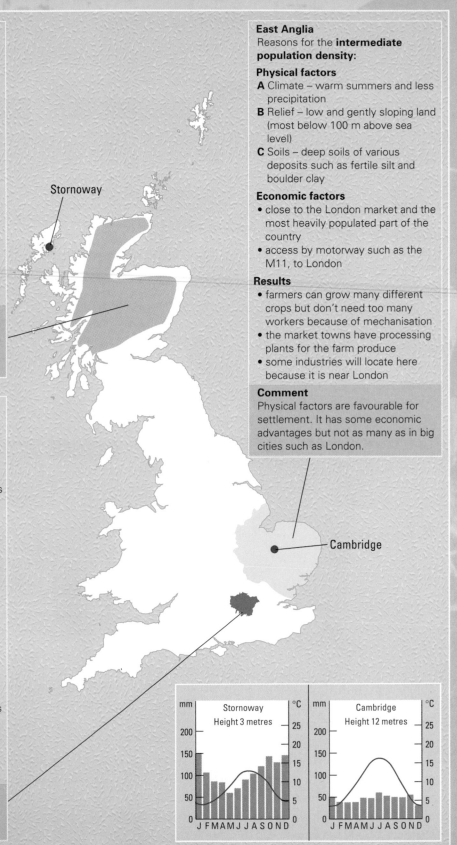

Stornoway

Cambridge

Stornoway
Height 3 metres

Cambridge
Height 12 metres

Internal migration
the United Kingdom

Source 1 shows the average population change for the different regions in Great Britain that was revealed by the census taken in 1991. Scotland and all the regions in the north of England lost people, while most regions in the south and east of England increased in population. This suggests that the long-established migration of people from the North to the South was still taking place (Source 2).

Source 1 | Population change 1981–91

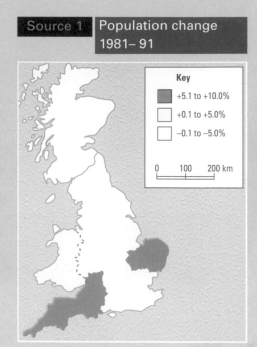

Source 2 | Migration movements

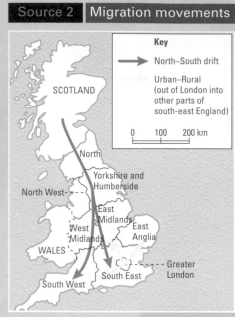

Source 3 | Population change by county 1981–91

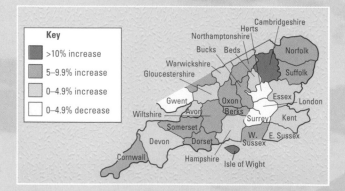

Source 4 | Population change in the English conurbations, 1981–91

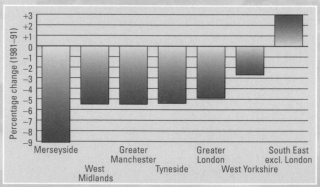

The map in Source 3 gives more detail about population changes for southern England because it is based upon county statistics. This map highlights more clearly the way in which Greater London has lost population, while counties to the north and west of London have grown the most. This change in population can be explained by the process of **urban to rural migration**. The push and pull factors for this were given in Source 4 on page 99.

Planners have also played their part in encouraging this movement. There are restrictions upon building new houses in the Green Belt which surrounds London. New towns, located outside London, were selected as growth points. Much of the population increase in Buckinghamshire is concentrated in the 'new town' of Milton Keynes. Urban to rural migration is taking place from all the other English conurbations as well; it is not unique to Greater London (Source 4).

Source 1	Age dependency ratios for EU countries

Age dependency ratio

persons 65 + as % of persons aged 15-64

	1990	2040
Belgium	21.9	41.5
Denmark	22.2	43.4
France	21.9	39.2
Germany	23.7	47.1
Greece	20.5	41.7
Ireland	18.4	27.2
Italy	20.4	48.4
Luxembourg	20.4	41.2
Netherlands	17.4	48.5
Portugal	16.4	38.9
Spain	17.0	41.7
UK	23.5	39.1
EU	**21.4**	**42.8**

One population prediction that it is safe to make about EU countries is that their populations will grow much older over the next 40 years. Within the EU the number of people aged 65 and over is expected to rise from 50 to 75 millions between 1990 and 2040. Also the percentage of persons aged 65 and over will increase relative to those of working age between 15 and 64 (Source 1).

As Source 1 shows, France is close to the EU averages. Further information about France is given in Source 2.

Source 2	France

A

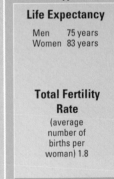

Life Expectancy

Men 75 years
Women 83 years

Total Fertility Rate
(average number of births per woman) 1.8

B

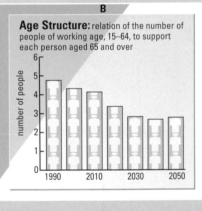

Age Structure: relation of the number of people of working age, 15–64, to support each person aged 65 and over

number of people

1990 2010 2030 2050

C

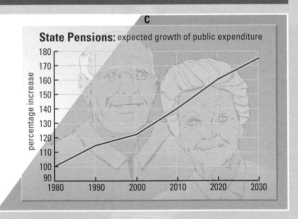

State Pensions: expected growth of public expenditure

percentage increase

1980 1990 2000 2010 2020 2030

There are two reasons why France's population is ageing (Source 2A).

1 Life expectancy is high. People are living longer as medical technology improves.

2 The fertility rate is low. To replace the population, the fertility rate needs to be 2.1 births during the lifetime of a woman.

The result is that there are fewer people of working age to support the elderly. In 1990 there were almost five people of working age to support one retired person (Source 2B); by 2040 there will be under three.

A big increase in what the state pays out in pensions is expected (Source 2C). At the same time as fewer people are earning money by working, more people will be drawing a state pension. Those working will need to pay higher taxes to support the great army of over 65s. It is an increasing worry for the French government as to where the money will come from, just as it is for all the EU governments. But it is not all gloom. Parts of the economy will benefit. Surveys in France show that some old people are quite wealthy and keen to spend money on leisure, holidays and health care.

Population contrasts
The USA and Mexico

It is interesting to compare the population characteristics and movements of countries with different levels of economic development. Here we look at Mexico and the USA. Source 1 examines the basic population data, while Source 2 shows the population structure. Source 3 looks at the economic and social data for each country.

Source 1 | **Basic population data**

	USA	Mexico
Birth rate (per 1000 per year)	16	28
Death rate (per 1000 per year)	9	6
Rate of natural increase (% per year)	0.7	2.2
Percentage of married women using birth control methods	74	53

Comment

USA – slow population growth; it will take 100 years for the population to double.

Mexico – fast population growth; it will take only 31 years for the population to double.

Source 2 | **Population structure: population pyramids for the USA and Mexico**

Comment
The USA has a high proportion of old people and has the problems of an ageing population.

Comment
Mexico has a high proportion of young people and the problems of a fast growing population.

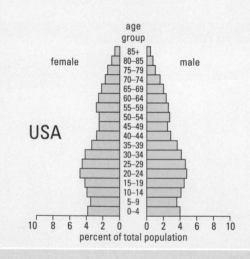

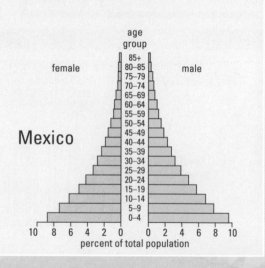

Source 3 | **Economic and social data**

Non-population data	USA	Mexico
GDP per head (in US$)	23 120	3 470
Unemployment rate (%)	8	28
Number of people per doctor	500	2000
Life expectancy at birth	76	70
Infant mortality rate (per 1000)	8	35

Comment

These economic and social statistics confirm how much better developed economically the USA is than Mexico. The differences explain why so many Mexicans migrate to the USA.

Source 4 | Present-day migrations in the USA

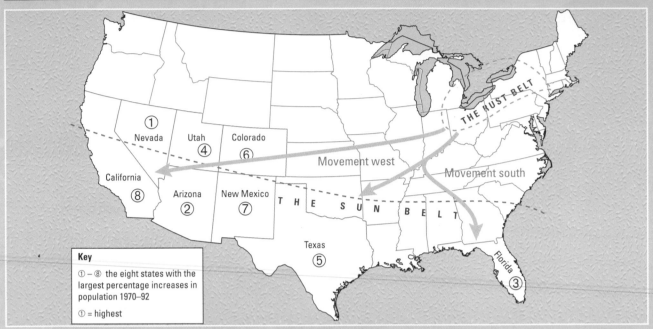

Key
① – ⑧ the eight states with the largest percentage increases in population 1970–92
① = highest

Internal migration in the USA

There are two main migrations flows:

1 **Urban–rural** – out of the big cities and into the small towns and country areas around the cities.

2 **'Rust belt' to 'sun belt'** (Source 4) – the name 'rust belt' conveys the image of old factories being closed down, machinery being allowed to rust in the old steel and engineering works and resulting unemployment. In the 'sun belt' it is warm all year, and a different world in winter to the cold and snowy north-east. Many retired people have been attracted there. So too have high-technology companies, which have increased the number of jobs.

Source 5 | On the border

Internal migration in Mexico

One type of migration dominates – rural to urban. All roads lead to Mexico City. It is the capital city. It has the head offices of the main Mexican companies. There are more industries here than in any other city. With a population of around 20 million, it is now ten times larger than the next largest city. This means that no other city can be as attractive for new economic development.

International migration

This is from Mexico to the USA. At least 2 million people, most of them illegal immigrants, are estimated to cross the land border which separates wealth and poverty every year. Most Mexicans in the USA only find unskilled work on farms, in the food processing factories, on the building sites and in the hotels and cafés. By American standards the work is low paid. By Mexican standards it is well paid, which is a good economic reason for Mexicans to carry on trying to beat the border patrols (Source 5).

Activities

1 Give the differences between each of the following:
   a distribution and density of population
   b physical and human factors.

2 Look at the world map (Source 1).

| Source 1 | World map |

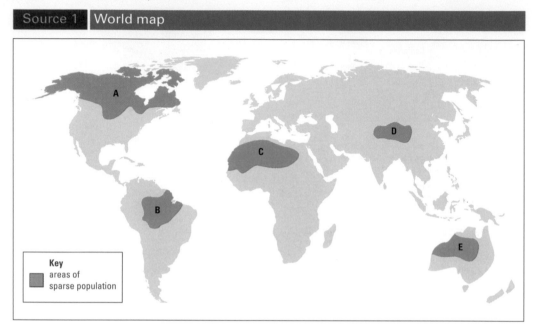

Key
areas of sparse population

   a i Name the area labelled A.
      ii Describe the factors which help to explain why it is sparsely populated.
   b i Name the areas lettered C and E.
      ii What do they have in common to explain why they are sparsely populated?
   c For either area B or area D, find out the reasons why it is sparsely populated.

3 a Name the continent with
      i the highest average birth rate
      ii the lowest average birth rate.
   b Suggest reasons for the difference in the size of the birth rate between them.
   c i Explain why death rates have declined everywhere in the world.
      ii How has this decline affected world population change?
   d From Source 2 on page 96 work out the rates of natural increase for Asia and North America. Show your working.

4 Briefly explain the differences between the following types of migration:
   a compulsory and voluntary
   b international and internal
   c permanent and temporary.

5 a Name one natural hazard.
   b Explain how this hazard might cause migration.

6 Illustrating your answers with labelled sketches:
  a give reasons for rural to urban migration in less economically developed countries
  b explain why urban to rural migration is of greater importance in the more economically developed countries.

7 Source 2 is a population pyramid for Australia.

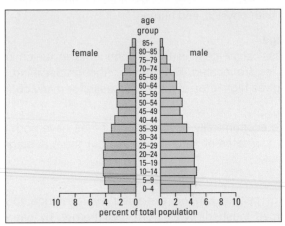

Source 2 | **Australia: population structure**

a Work out from the graph the percentages of people over 65 and under 15.
  b Explain why these age groups are known as dependants.
  c Australia has an ageing population. Describe the problems this may cause.

8 **a** What is meant by the term 'conurbation'?
  b Name one British conurbation and explain why high densities of population are found inside it.

9 Suggest reasons for the differences between the USA and Mexico using the following headings: Birth rates, Population increase, Population structure.

10 Mexico is an example of a LEDC.
  a Describe the main type of migration found there today.
  b Explain by referring to push and pull factors why this migration is taking place.
  c What problems may be caused by this migration?

11 Look at the photograph in Source 3.

Source 3 | Otz valley in Austria

a Describe the physical features and land uses shown.
  b Suggest reasons for the uneven distribution of people in the area shown on the photograph.

1 Distribution and density of population

The world's population is unevenly spread across the earth's surface. The negative factors which lead to low densities of population are often physical factors such as climate and relief. To explain high densities of population it is usually necessary to study a variety of factors both physical and human.

2 Population change

Population increase is greatest in those continents in which many less economically developed countries are located. Birth rates, although declining, remain higher than the death rates; this gives high rates of natural increase for many countries in Africa, Asia and South America.

Most of the more economically developed countries have both low birth rates and low death rates; their low rates of natural increase put them in stage 4 of the demographic transition model.

3 Migration

The movement of people can be explained by reference to push and pull factors. Refugees are forced (pushed) away from their homes by natural or human disasters. Many people move because they are pulled by the attractions of another place. In LEDCs many people prefer to live in the cities, whereas in MEDCs an increasing number of people are being attracted back towards the rural areas.

4 Population structure

Population pyramids are used to show a country's or a town's population structure. The wide base to the pyramids of LEDCs reflects their high birth rates. The narrower, more straight up and down shape to the pyramids of MEDCs reflects their low birth rates and the greater proportion of old people.

In LEDCs the main population problem is how to cope with high rates of population increase. In MEDCs the problem is making adequate provision for the larger numbers of old people.

5 Population distribution: the United Kingdom

The uneven spread of people across the UK is identified. The variations in density between three regions of the UK are explained by reference to physical, economic and historical factors.

6 Internal migration: the United Kingdom

The two main types of migration are identified. One is the continuing drift of people from north to south. The other is urban to rural migration. Both have contributed to the general increase in population (except for Greater London) in the area lying south of the Severn–Wash line.

7 An ageing population: France

France is typical of EU countries in having an increasingly high proportion of its population over the age of 65 years. There are some financial worries for the future as the pensions and health care for more people who are old have to be paid for by fewer people who are working.

Settlement

Chicago, the home of the sky scraper

The nature and growth of settlements

A **settlement** is a place where people live and work. Settlements may be classified using different factors (Source 1 and 2). When settlements are put into order of size and importance, a **hierarchy** of settlements is produced.

Classification of settlements

A Rural or urban	B Size	C Function	D Area served
capital city	above 2 million	Government, HQs of companies, big shops, finance, tourists	serves whole country
conurbation	500 000 – 2 million	industry, offices, shops	large area around it
regional centre	150 000 – 500 000	HQs of local companies, shops, offices, industry	its own region
industrial town	25 000 – 150 000	industry, shops	local area around it
market town (small town)	2 500 – 25 000	shops and local services	small local area
village	100 – 2 500	basic services e.g. pub, church, shop	only the farms outside the village
hamlet	10 – 100	no services	no services
isolated farm	less than 10 people	no services	no services

URBAN / RURAL

Settlements which are small and in the middle of countryside are **rural**. Those which are large and provide services for the areas around them are **urban**. The market town, which serves the rural area around it, is the smallest urban settlement.	There are thousands of small settlements in the United Kingdom such as farms, hamlets and villages, but there is only one capital city (Source 2). This is why Source 1 has the shape of a pyramid.	This is the purpose of a settlement – why it is there and what job it does. All settlements are places for people to live, but most settlements have other functions. The larger the settlement, the greater the number and the more varied its functions.	The area served by a settlement is called its **sphere of influence**. London's sphere of influence is the whole country. It has some functions, such as Government, which are not found in any other city. Outside London there are regional centres such as Norwich serving East Anglia and Plymouth serving south-west England.

The range of settlement in the UK – a farm in Upper Teesdale, and London

Location and change

The **site** of a settlement includes the features of its specific location. The **situation** of a settlement is its location in relation to its surrounding area. Settlements were originally located with great care (Source 3). The factors taken into consideration for selecting a settlement site in the UK included:

- water supply – access to a reliable source of fresh water
- drainage – freedom from flooding
- aspect – facing south for sun and warmth
- shelter – protected from cold or strong winds by high ground
- resources – next to good farmland or a mineral source such as coal
- special features – such as an easy bridging point across a river or a steep hill for defence.

Source 3	Sites for settlements

Many settlements have changed through time. Those with a favourable situation are likely to have grown and changed their function. For example, some villages favourably situated near the meeting point of roads grew to become market towns. Others situated next to coalfields became mining villages or even grew into industrial towns. Those settlements that have stayed as small villages may also have changed their function. No longer are the majority of people living in villages in the UK directly connected with farming. They are more likely to be **commuters**. This change in function from farming to commuting village may bring new problems and conflicts. Some villages in the UK have declined in population, notably those affected by closure of the coal mines.

Patterns of land use

Urban land uses include shops, offices, factories, transport, recreation and waste land. However, the land use which covers the largest amount of land is housing. The term **morphology** is used to describe the layout of an urban area and the way in which the land uses are arranged within it. In most British cities it is possible to recognise three **urban zones** based upon location and land uses (Source 1).

Source 1	Urban zones in British towns

Urban zone	Location and appearance	Land use characteristics
CBD (Central Business District)	* city centre * tall buildings including skyscrapers containing offices * high building density with little open space	* old buildings, e.g. cathedral, castle * many shops of different types including department stores * company offices, banks and building societies * places of entertainment such as theatres and night clubs
Inner city (also known as the twilight zone or the zone of transition)	* around the edge of the city centre * unattractive, run-down appearance with many old buildings, made worse by vandalism and graffiti	* factories and warehouses * residential – often terraced houses and high-rise flats * universities and hospitals * inner ring roads * small shopping centres selling everyday convenience goods
Residential suburbs	* all the outer areas up to the edge of the built-up area * generally smarter appearance in the outer suburbs * some areas of open space	* residential – with the houses increasing in size, becoming more recent, changing from terraced to semi-detached and detached towards the outskirts * small shopping centres selling everyday convenience goods

Urban models

Various **urban models** have been devised to show the general arrangement of land use zones in cities (Source 2).

The Burgess model (Model 1) shows a circular pattern of land uses around the CBD. This model uses five zones because the inner city and residential suburbs have each been subdivided into two. The Hoyt model (Model 2) uses the circles of the Burgess model as its base but then adds sectors to show that similar land uses are concentrated in certain parts of the urban area. For example, factories may be concentrated in one area to form a zone of industry. A sector containing many high-priced houses may follow the line of a main road resulting in the formation of a high-class residential area for the wealthy. The Burgess and Hoyt models had to be adapted to show the general land use patterns in cities in the less economically developed countries. Model 3 includes the inner city slums and shanty towns which house many people.

There are three explanations for these land use patterns.

1 Historical

The urban area expanded outwards from the original site which is where the city centre is found today.

2 Economic

Rents and rates in the CBD became too expensive for people. In the suburbs there was more land and it was cheaper. Only businesses could afford to stay in the CBD, but even they needed to make the most of expensive land by building upwards.

3 Concentrations of similar land uses

One part of the urban area may have all the advantages for industrial location so that a lot of factories want to locate there; but few people want to live next door to a factory, so the residential areas are located elsewhere. Planners also prefer this **segregation of land uses** into definite zones.

Source 2 Urban models for land use patterns

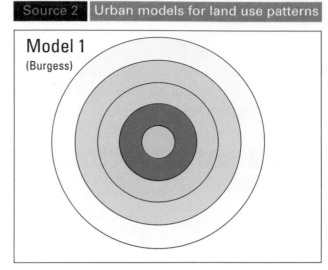

Model 1
(Burgess)

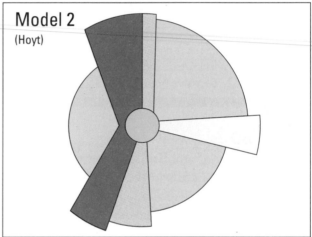

Model 2
(Hoyt)

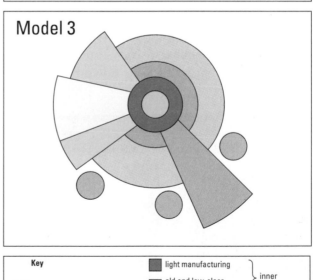

Model 3

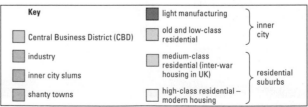

Key

- ☐ Central Business District (CBD)
- ☐ industry
- ☐ inner city slums
- ☐ shanty towns
- ☐ light manufacturing ⎫
- ☐ old and low-class residential ⎬ inner city
- ☐ medium-class residential (inter-war housing in UK) ⎫ residential
- ☐ high-class residential – modern housing ⎬ suburbs

7.3 Changing cities

Cities are dynamic places which are constantly changing. Some areas within them are growing or expanding. Others may be losing population.

Source 1	Changes in the city centre and the reasons for them

Change	Reason for change
skyscraper office blocks	shortage and high price of land
inner ring roads	traffic congestion
one-way streets	traffic congestion
improvements in public transport:	too much use of the car for travelling
bus lanes	to work and for shopping,
trams	parking problems
metro links between buses and cars	air pollution: photochemical smog
park and ride schemes	and low-level ozone
shopping streets pedestrianised	conflicts between shoppers and motorists
indoor shopping centres	

In the CBD

Visit the centre of any British city after a gap of a few years and you can hardly recognise it. Familiar old buildings have been knocked down to make room for skyscraper office developments. Main shopping streets have been pedestrianised. Indoor shopping centres have been built. Multi-storey car parks have been provided as part of city centre redevelopment schemes. New one-way street systems have changed traffic flows through the centre. You should be able to notice some of these changes in the city centre nearest to your home. What all these changes are designed to do is to overcome city centre problems (Source 1). There is more urgency than ever to improve city centres because many of the functions of the traditional city centre are being threatened by out-of-town developments for shopping and business (see page 119).

Source 2	The environment can be grim in the inner city

In the inner city

Many inner city areas are depressing places in which change has usually meant decline and decay (Source 2). City authorities and businesses have invested in the CBD. Much less has been spent in the inner city and here the environment is a growing problem. Large areas of waste land have become dumping grounds. Big factories are derelict monuments of the Industrial Revolution. Terraced houses, built for the better-off people in Victorian times, are now derelict and boarded up. Empty buildings are favourite targets for vandals and paint sprayers.

Economic decline follows. Those who could afford it have moved out, leaving behind the unemployed and the unskilled on low wages. Crime rates are high. The social character of the area has changed. Concentrations of people from the ethnic minorities are found in many inner cities. The numbers of pensioners, one-parent families and students are also above average.

You may find it hard to believe that in the 1960s planners believed that moving residents into high-rise blocks of flats was the solution to the problem of slum housing. The people who were forced to live in these flats had very different views (Source 3)!

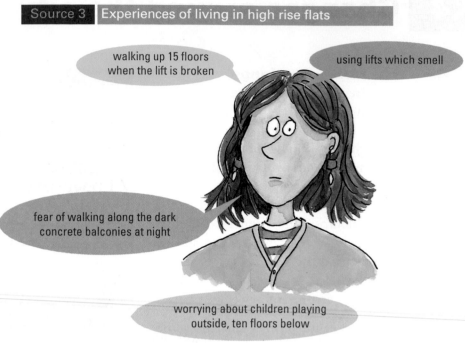

Source 3 | Experiences of living in high rise flats

walking up 15 floors when the lift is broken

using lifts which smell

fear of walking along the dark concrete balconies at night

worrying about children playing outside, ten floors below

Source 4 | Salford Quays

There are many schemes for inner city renewal, such as the City Challenge in which local authorities work with other local interest groups, supported by government money, to build new houses and community facilities. The Enterprise Zone idea was used to attract investment into redevelopment of the Docklands in the East End of London. The old Manchester Dock basins were landscaped and luxury houses were built around them. Now their name is Salford Quays (Source 4). Improving housing in inner city areas to make it more attractive to richer people is called **gentrification**. The problem with this and with all the other schemes is that only a tiny proportion of inner city residents feel any benefits.

Changes around the city

The rural-urban fringe

The area around the edge of a city is known as the **rural-urban fringe**. It is where the green fields and open spaces of the countryside meet the continuously built-up areas of the city. Countryside has been lost by the continued outward growth of cities and their suburbs. The open land around the edge of a city is in great demand for housing, industry, shopping, recreation and the needs of the public utilities, such as reservoirs and sewerage works.

One reason for growth and change in the rural-urban fringe is a feeling of dissatisfaction with the city.

- Houses are close together with few open spaces.
- Air quality is poor.
- Companies find that there is a shortage of land for building new offices and factories.

These are all **push factors**. There are also **pull factors** on the city edge.

- Land is cheaper so houses are larger.
- Factories can be more spacious and have plenty of room for workers to park their cars.
- Closeness to the main roads and motorways allows for quicker and easier customer contacts.
- New developments on the outskirts of the city are favoured by the greater personal mobility

Source 1 | Conflicts of interest between farmers and developers

People from the town trample on my crops.

I have lost half of my farmland to builders.

Businesses can make more profit if they are next to motorways.

My farm is split into two parts by the motorway.

The public want to shop in out of town centres where parking is free and easy.

allowed by the car.

Not everyone is happy with the continued loss of countryside around the cities. Many environmentalists are very concerned. There are often conflicts of interest, such as between farmers and developers (Source 1). People who have spent all their lives in villages resent the changes which they are faced with as villages grow into commuter settlements (Source 2).

Source 2 | Changes in a village as it becomes a commuter settlement

number of people in the village

300
250
200
150
100
50
0
1960 1970 1980 1990

average price of the old houses in the village

60 000
£
30 000
1960 1970 1980 1990

average number of cars passing through the village each day

160
120
80
40
1960 1970 1980 1990

change in morphology

new estate

old village

Key
■ old houses
□ new houses
— road

Retailing

In the more economically developed countries there has been a great increase in **out-of-town retailing,** with large purpose-built **superstores** and shopping centres located in the rural-urban fringe. The number of superstores has increased dramatically in the United Kingdom since 1980 (Source 3). It is easy to understand why. More people own their own cars. The large car parks are free. Access is easy because the shopping centres are located next to main roads and motorway junctions. In contrast, city centre shoppers face traffic congestion and expensive parking. Also the larger centres have shopping malls which are bright and modern with everything under one roof. Other facilities, such as multi-screen cinemas or bowling alleys, are often included within the shopping centre, or are located close by, so that there is something there for all the family (Source 4).

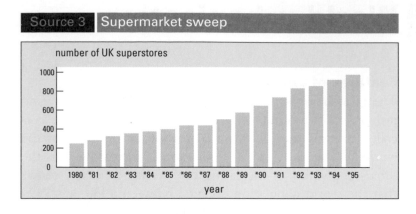

Source 3 Supermarket sweep

number of UK superstores

Source 4 Out-of-town shopping centre near Durham

Source 5 Shopping hierarchy

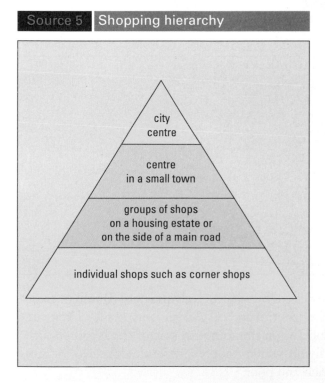

Out-of-town shopping centres do not fit the traditional **hierarchy** of shopping centres found in the UK (Source 5). At the bottom of the hierarchy is the corner shop, where everyday goods, such as milk, newspapers and sweets, known as **convenience goods,** are bought. These are **low-order goods,** used often, for which most people are prepared to travel only a short distance.

At the top of the hierarchy is the city centre. This is where people go to buy clothes or to have a look around department stores. Many of the goods sold in department stores, such as clothes, electrical items and furniture, are **comparison goods.** People buy these less often and are willing to travel further to buy them. The department store has a high **threshold.** A large number of people must shop there for the store to be profitable. It has a large **sphere of influence:** people travel from some distance away to shop there, helped by the fact that the city centre is the focus for the main roads and most bus and rail services.

119

World urbanisation

Features of urbanisation

The growth of towns and cities which leads to an increasing proportion of a country's population living in urban areas is called **urbanisation.** Cities are growing in size all over the world. While the world's population is increasing fast, the urban population is increasing even faster. Source 1 shows that the world population doubled between 1950 and 1990 but that the urban population trebled.

What is significant about present-day rates of urbanisation is the difference in the speed of growth between the cities in the more economically developed countries and those in the less economically developed countries. The rate of city growth is much higher in the LEDCs (Source 2) so that the number of urban dwellers is now greater than in the MEDCs. Present trends are expected to continue.

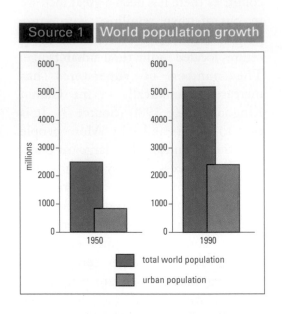

Source 1 | World population growth

- total world population
- urban population

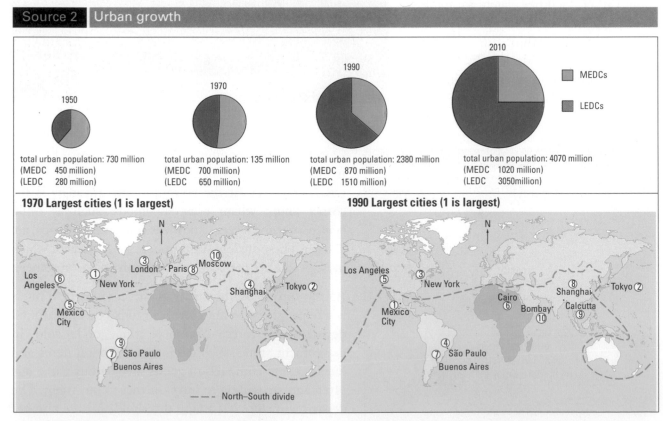

Source 2 | Urban growth

total urban population: 730 million
(MEDC 450 million)
(LEDC 280 million)

total urban population: 135 million
(MEDC 700 million)
(LEDC 650 million)

total urban population: 2380 million
(MEDC 870 million)
(LEDC 1510 million)

total urban population: 4070 million
(MEDC 1020 million)
(LEDC 3050million)

1970 Largest cities (1 is largest)

1990 Largest cities (1 is largest)

- - - North–South divide

This means that the distribution of the world's big cities is changing. Source 2 shows the world's top ten cities by size for 1970 and 1990. Three have dropped out of the top ten – London, Paris and Moscow. All are in Europe. They have been replaced by Cairo, Calcutta and Bombay from the continents of Africa and Asia. They are located on the southern side of the North–South divide which roughly separates the world into rich and poor.

The size of big cities is another feature of world urbanisation. For many years the **millionaire city** (a city of more than one million people) was considered a big city, especially since in 1900 there were only two – London and Paris. Now there are over 300 (Source 3).

Each of the top ten cities now has more than ten million people. The use of the term 'mega city' may be more appropriate. Mexico City is the world's biggest city with a population of up to 20 million (Source 4). This one city has more people living in it than live in many of the countries of Central and South America!

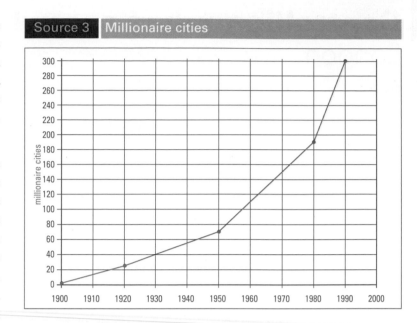

| Source 3 | Millionaire cities |

| Source 4 | Mexico City, the largest of them all |

Causes of urbanisation

Urban growth has always been associated with economic development. As a country increases in wealth, fewer people work in primary activities such as farming and forestry in the rural areas. Increasing numbers of people now work in secondary (manufacturing) and tertiary (service) occupations, which are overwhelmingly concentrated in urban areas.

High rates of urbanisation in LEDCs occur because:

- most new economic developments are concentrated in the big cities
- push and pull factors lead to high rates of rural to urban migration.
- cities experience high rates of natural increase of population.

121

Countryside in Britain has been lost to urban areas at an alarming rate since the 1930s. The outward growth of London has been on a different scale to that of other cities within the United Kingdom. As long ago as the late 1940s planners realised that something needed to be done to stop the continued growth of London. Two measures were tried (Source 1):

- declaring a **green belt** around London, within which most types of new development were forbidden.
- building **new towns** beyond the green belt.

As the slum properties in the inner city regions were cleared, people had to be rehoused somewhere. Eight new towns (named on Source 1) were originally planned as growth points with houses, shops, offices and factories. They were located far enough from London to stop the continuous **urban sprawl.** The intention was to make them as self-contained as possible, with their own places of work, to discourage residents from commuting into London. Milton Keynes is an example of a later and larger new town which has attracted people and companies.

Planning policies change over time. In recent years attempts have been made to renovate and to redevelop some of the inner city areas within London to make them more attractive places in which to live and work. This helps to reduce the pressure for growth around the edge of Greater London. Although the Docklands development in the East End is the largest example of this, in other inner city areas houses are being improved to increase their attractiveness as residential neighbourhoods (Source 2). This is another example of the process of gentrification referred to on page 117.

What planners have discovered, however, is that stopping urban expansion is not easy. The pressures

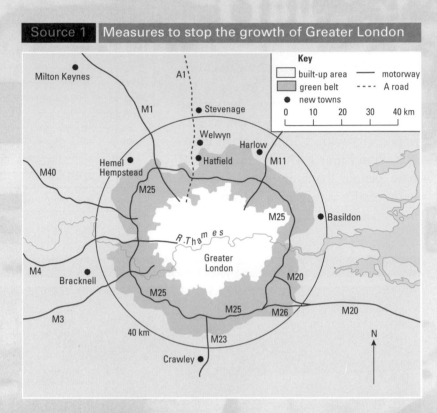

Source 1 Measures to stop the growth of Greater London

Key
built-up area — motorway
green belt ---- A road
● new towns
0 10 20 30 40 km

Milton Keynes
A1
M1
Stevenage
Welwyn
Harlow
Hemel Hempstead
Hatfield
M11
M40
M25
M25
Basildon
R. Thames
Greater London
M4
Bracknell
M25
M20
M25
M26
M20
M3
40 km
M23
Crawley
N

Source 2 Improved housing in London

for development do not go away. The M25 motorway, constructed around London on Green Belt land, is a magnet for developers. Just think of the advantages of a location next to the M25 for a company which markets its goods throughout the UK.

An out-of-town shopping centre
the MetroCentre, Gateshead

The first of the big out-of-town shopping centres to be built in the United Kingdom was the MetroCentre near Gateshead (Source 1). It was followed by others, such as Meadowhall near Sheffield and Lakeside in Essex. The MetroCentre is located within 6 km of the main shopping areas of Newcastle-upon-Tyne and Gateshead (Source 1). It occupies 50 hectares of what was largely waste and derelict land along the south bank of the River Tyne – land that was relatively cheap to buy.

The MetroCentre brought new ideas to UK retailing:

- It created an artificial indoor environment which brought new comforts to shoppers all year round.
- It provided the full range of types of retail outlet with everything from department stores such as Marks and Spencer to small specialist shops such as model shops.
- It included leisure facilities such as a multi-screen cinema and superbowl, as well as restaurants and street cafés.
- It is surrounded by open car parks and there are also multi-storey car parks.

The MetroCentre is now so large and so popular that there are now direct bus services from most towns in the North of England. Its sphere of influence, therefore, now extends westwards across to Carlisle and southwards to Harrogate and York.

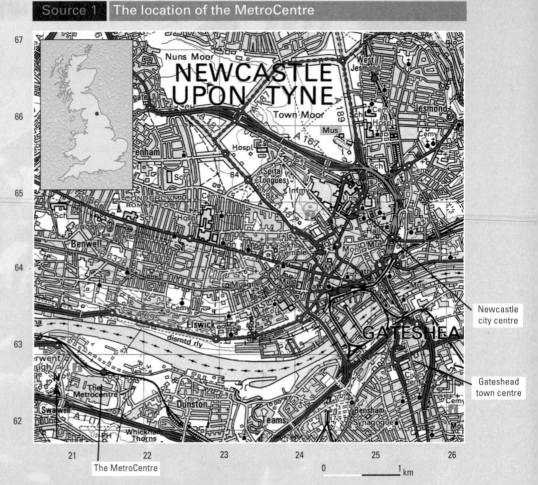

Source 1 The location of the MetroCentre

Newcastle city centre

Gateshead town centre

The MetroCentre

0 ___ 1 km

Fact File MetroCentre

- The MetroCentre opened in 1988.
- There are 335 shops under one roof.
- The MetroCentre has an 11-screen cinema, its own fun park, 28 lanes of tenpin bowling and more than 50 restaurants and cafés.
- The MetroCentre now includes a hotel and conference centre, exhibition centre and office block.
- There are more than half a million visitors each week.
- Total visitors hit a record of over 27 million in 1995.
- The MetroCentre is well placed next to the main A1 road.
- 85 trains per day stop at the MetroCentre.
- The Centre's own bus station handles over 1000 bus movements a day.

A European city
Paris

Paris, a city of 8.7 million people, is the capital of France. It has a clear urban structure, which is built around its Central Business District.

The CBD of any city is usually easy to recognise because of the height and density of its buildings. Some of the distinctive areas that can be identified within the CBD of Paris are shown in Source 1. Paris has a historical core on the Ile de la Cité (I) in the middle of the River Seine where the Cathedral of Notre Dame and the law courts are located.

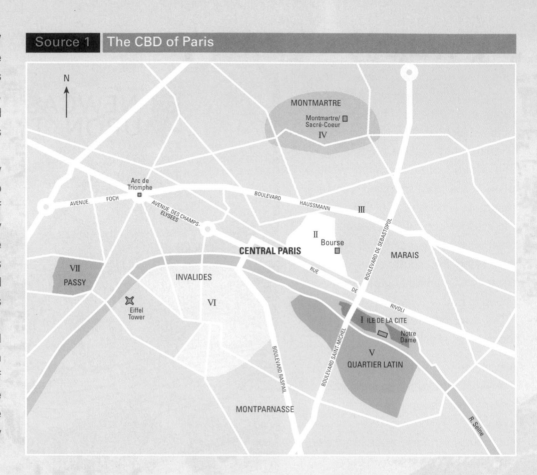

Source 1 The CBD of Paris

Source 2 Paris city centre

On the northern side (or Right Bank) of the River Seine is the main business and financial district with the stock exchange (Bourse) and headquarters of the big banks (II). Just to the north is the main shopping area where the streets, such as Boulevard Haussmann (III), are lined by department stores and boutiques. A short distance further north is Montmartre, which is an area noted for eating and entertainment (IV).

On the southern side (or Left Bank) of the River Seine is the Latin Quarter (V), which is the educational centre with many universities, museums and bookshops. Between the Latin Quarter and the Eiffel Tower (Source 2) is the political zone; most of the land and property is government owned (VI). Therefore the areas of greatest importance economically, politically and culturally are located close to the river and they form the core of the CBD of Paris.

Towards the western, eastern and southern edges of the CBD, there are more extensive residential areas. The areas in the west benefit from closeness to the Bois de Boulogne (a large area of open space) and contain the most expensive properties (VII).

Urban transport in Paris

Most workplaces and places of interest to visitors are concentrated in the city centre, but the majority of Parisians live in the suburbs of Paris. Many more people actually live in settlements beyond the edge of the built-up area.

In Paris, the places where people work are highly concentrated. Most workplaces lie west of the Ile de la Cité (its location is shown in Source 1) but most of the people live to the east. There are many jobs in central Paris, and more than 3 million commuters every working day. What this means is that the rush hour traffic in Paris starts earlier and lasts longer than in many other cities. Traffic congestion is a particular problem.

Source 3	The Paris métro network

Source 4	Motorways in and around Paris

Urban transport systems are vital to big cities such as Paris.

- Within the central areas the métro (underground railway) has a dense network of lines (Source 3.).
- Above ground the métro is supported by bus routes in the inner areas and French railways (SNCF) into the suburbs.
- Since 1965 a new express métro called the RER (Réseau Express Régional) has been built at a deeper level than the old métro system. The electric trains travel at speeds up to 90 km per hour, with fewer stops, to give a quick way of crossing Paris. The RER system links up with the old métro system in the centre and French railways in the suburbs. Its most recent extension has been eastwards to the Disneyland Paris Resort.

Over one-third of daily commuters into Paris continue to use their own cars. Since 1965 over 800 km of new urban motorways have been built (Source 4). Around the CBD is the inner ring road, known as the 'Périphérique'. Around the northern and eastern edges is the outer ring road, the A86 'L'autoroute urbaine'.

This road is equivalent to the M25 around London and has all the same problems!

Urban transect
Manchester

In this unit we are going to follow a **transect** through Manchester to explore how land use changes. The transect runs north to south from Manchester city centre to the River Mersey along one of the main roads in and out of the city (Source 1).

Manchester's CBD shows up clearly on the map. It is where many main roads meet. The main railway and bus stations are found here, along with the city's main exhibition centre (G-MEX). The area is almost continuously built up with few open spaces.

The inner ring road which marks the southern boundary of Manchester's CBD is partly a motorway (in squares 8397 and 8497 on Source 1). The inner city begins to the south of this road. At first public buildings, particularly universities, hospitals and museums, take up a lot of the land, then residential land uses become more important from Moss Side and Rusholme southwards.

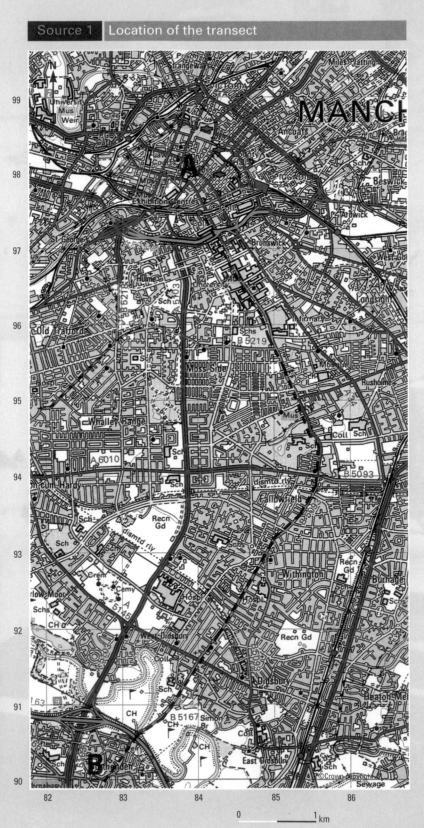

Source 1 | Location of the transect

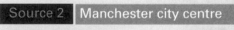

Source 2 | Manchester city centre

Source 3 | Rusholme shopping centre

Source 4	Census information about Rusholme, Fallowfield, Withington and Didsbury			
	RUSHOLME	**FALLOWFIELD**	**WITHINGTON**	**DIDSBURY**

Types of housing

	RUSHOLME	FALLOWFIELD	WITHINGTON	DIDSBURY
Detached	2.3%	5%	2.6%	8.2%
Semi-detached	34.3%	43%	48.8%	50.6%
Terraced	34.3%	24.9%	19.3%	15.3%
Flats	29.2%	27.1%	29.3%	25.9%

Ethnic group of the inhabitants

	RUSHOLME	FALLOWFIELD	WITHINGTON	DIDSBURY
White	68.8%	77.1%	87.2%	91.3%
Black	7.3%	6.7%	2.0%	1.0%
Asian	28.7%	13.0%	8.5%	5.9%
Other	4.2%	3.2%	2.4%	1.9%

Households without a car

RUSHOLME	FALLOWFIELD	WITHINGTON	DIDSBURY
56%	54%	42%	30%

Head of household working in a professional or managerial occupation

RUSHOLME	FALLOWFIELD	WITHINGTON	DIDSBURY
26%	22%	32%	44%

Out of work

RUSHOLME	FALLOWFIELD	WITHINGTON	DIDSBURY
22%	21%	13%	8%

Information about four of the wards along the transect route has been taken from the 1991 census (Source 4). It illustrates some of the ways in which the land uses and features of an urban area change between the city centre and the edge of the built-up area. Similar changes can be identified in most British cities.

What the information suggests is that Rusholme and Fallowfield have many of the features associated with the inner city. There are more terraced houses than further out in the suburbs of Manchester. Socially, there is a significant concentration of people from the ethnic minority groups, mainly Asian; some of the features of the local shopping centre reflect their presence (Source 3). Economically, people are less well off than those living in the suburbs. More are out of work and fewer have well-paid jobs. Lower rates of car ownership result from this.

Withington and Didsbury, on the other hand, show features which are associated with the residential suburbs. Didsbury is located nearer the edge of the city and is the wealthiest of the four wards. There is a significantly higher proportion of detached houses here.

Urban problems
less economically developed countries

In LEDCs, cities are seen as places of wealth and great opportunity, particularly when compared with living in the countryside. It is the speed at which the cities have grown that has led to many problems (Source 1).

São Paulo in Brazil, for example, grew by half a million people per year in the 1970s and 1980s. It is impossible to plan and to provide for such rapid growth.

Source 1 | Urban problems

1 Housing
Poor housing is the biggest urban problem. Self-help is the only option for most migrants to the city because they have no money. They must collect whatever free 'building materials' are available and build a shack on any empty land. Empty land is usually located around the edge of the city, but sometimes it exists within the city, such as next to a river with a high flood risk or on land too steep for normal building. Large numbers of people building their own shacks leads to the growth of a shanty town.

2 Provision of essential public services
The supply and distribution of water and electricity require a great deal of planning and investment. Most governments don't have the kind of money needed. Large areas of cities are not connected up to mains services. Power failures are frequent.

3 Unemployment
Many people have no regular work. Instead they scratch a living from the informal sector by selling vegetables and cigarettes on the streets or by collecting papers and plastic for recycling.

4 Traffic and transport
Public transport is usually overcrowded to bursting point. City-centre roads are often heavily congested with traffic. Controls on exhaust emissions are either non-existent or not enforced; there is air pollution.

70%

Casablanca, Morocco

40%

Mexico City

percentage in shanty towns

Lima, in Peru, is in many ways a typical capital city of one of the world's less economically developed countries. It has grown fast (Source 1) and the growth shows no sign of stopping as the countryside empties its surplus people. An increasing proportion of Lima's residents live in shanty towns (Source 2). Such shanty towns in Lima are called **barriadas** (Source 4).

The city is located in a desert and surrounded on its northern and eastern sides by low hills. These drab dry hills around the city were not farmed, and so this empty land has been used for homes by the new migrants into the city. Surveys among residents in the barriadas indicate that most have work, but perhaps only 10 per cent are in full-time jobs (Source 3).

There are a few examples within Lima of shanty towns that have been improved over time to become proper residential areas. One example is the township of Santiago near to the centre of Lima. This changed from a squatter settlement on empty land on the dried-up bed of an old river, to a normal residential area with all the public services and shops you would expect in any residential area. Good organisation among the residents and government help were essential in achieving this transformation. While not all of Lima's shanty towns will be able to do the same, Santiago's development does offer them some hope.

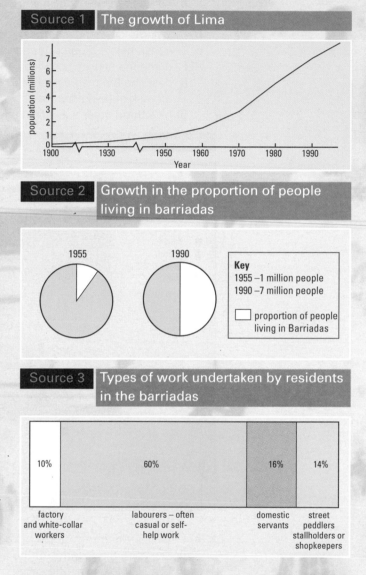

Source 1 — The growth of Lima

Source 2 — Growth in the proportion of people living in barriadas

1955   1990

Key
1955 – 1 million people
1990 – 7 million people

☐ proportion of people living in Barriadas

Source 3 — Types of work undertaken by residents in the barriadas

10%	60%	16%	14%
factory and white-collar workers	labourers – often casual or self-help work	domestic servants	street peddlers stallholders or shopkeepers

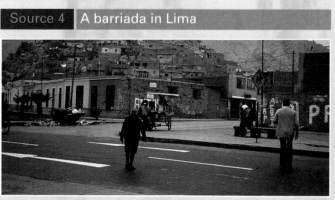

Source 4 — A barriada in Lima

1 a i Explain with the help of a diagram what is meant by a hierarchy of settlements.
    ii For the region in which you live, name examples of settlements for different levels in the hierarchy.
  b Give three differences between a village and a town.
  c The map below (Source 1) shows an English village. From the map:
    i name the services provided in the village
    ii describe the map evidence which suggests that the village should be free from the risk of being flooded
    iii give three other site advantages for this village.

Source 1 | An English village

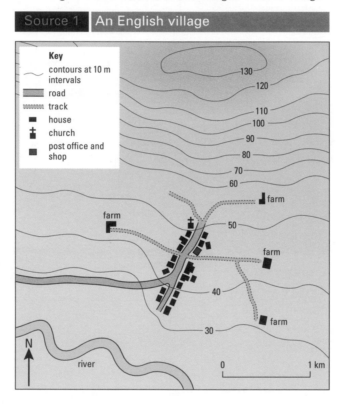

2 a i Define the terms 'urban morphology' and 'urban zone'.
    ii Describe the features of the CBD which make it a distinctive urban zone.
    iii Why is the city centre called the central business district?
  b i What are skyscrapers?
    ii Why are they built and who uses them?
  c i Describe the differences in types of housing between the inner city and residential suburbs.
    ii Give two reasons for the differences you have described in **c (i)**.

3 a i Describe the changes which have occurred in recent years, or are still occurring, in the centre of the city nearest to your home.
    ii Explain why these changes have occurred.
  b i Describe what makes the environment look so unattractive in the inner city areas.
    ii Why do some people refer to high-rise flats as a 'planning disaster'?
  c i What is meant by 'gentrification'?
    ii Why is it not a solution to the problems of every inner city area?

4 a Describe what is meant by the 'rural-urban fringe'.

   b Explain why it has become an attractive location for out-of-town shopping centres and business parks.

   c For either an environmentalist or a developer, write a speech for that person for use in a public meeting which has been called to discuss the proposals for building an out-of-town shopping centre in the rural-urban fringe.

5 a Give as many different pieces of evidence as you can find which show the cities are growing fast in the less economically developed countries of the world.

   b With the help of information from other units in this book, explain as fully as you can the reasons why cities in LEDCs are growing so quickly today.

6 a Give details about the attempts that have been made to stop the outward sprawl of London.

   b Why have they not been totally successful?

7 a Find out about the road and public transport systems in and around London.

   b List the similarities and differences between the urban transport systems of Paris and London.

8 a Describe the changes in Manchester between the city centre and the edge of the built-up area for the following headings: House type; Ethnic make-up; Wealth.

   b Explain where Rusholme and Didsbury would fit in the Burgess model of urban zones (see page 115).

   c i Describe the features of the layout of Moss Side shown in Source 2, including making suggestions about the types of housing.

     ii Name the urban zone in which Moss Side lies (see unit 7.2) and explain your answer.

Source 2 | **Moss Side**

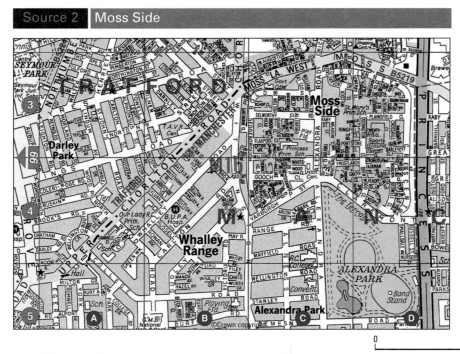

0   500m

9 a Make brief notes about the urban problems of cities in less economically developed countries.

   b Explain why slums and shanty towns in LEDCs may be:

     i places of despair

     ii places of hope.

1 The nature and growth of settlements

Settlements can be classified in different ways. The location for all settlements was chosen with great care. The size and functions of settlements change with time.

2 Patterns of land use

Within urban areas different land uses are concentrated in certain areas. A simple subdivision for most towns and cities in Britain is: city centre (CBD), inner city and residential suburbs. The general arrangement of land uses can be shown by urban models.

3 Changing cities

City centres and inner cities are areas of great change. Both urban zones display the effects of decline and renewal. Meanwhile, the rural-urban fringe is attracting many users from inside the city. A pleasant environment, nearness to main roads and low land costs have increased its attractiveness for out of town shopping centres.

4 World urbanisation

In earlier decades urbanisation was mainly a feature of the geography of the more economically developed countries. Today urbanisation is taking place at great speed in the less economically developed countries, creating some of the world's biggest cities.

5 Controlling urban sprawl: London

Measures taken during the last 50 years have controlled the growth and sprawl of London; much of the new growth has been concentrated in new towns beyond the London Green Belt.

6 An out-of-town shopping centre: the MetroCentre, Gateshead

This is the largest out-of-town shopping centre in the United Kingdom. Visiting the MetroCentre is an experience which millions of people have enjoyed. In March 1996 an ambitious extension plan was announced for up to 30 new shops and 2000 extra car parking spaces; these will increase still more the MetroCentre's already impressive record.

7 A European city: Paris

Within the CBD of big cities such as Paris, it is possible to recognise certain areas where particular functions are concentrated, such as finance and business on the north bank of the River Seine, and administration and government on the south bank.

Paris also has a dense network of public transport routes in the central areas, both underground and on the surface, which are interconnected. Even so, the inner and outer ring roads are both in constant use with many commuters using their own cars.

8 Urban transect: Manchester

The transect from the city centre of Manchester to the southern suburbs illustrates the types of changes in land uses and socio-economic characteristics that are likely to be found in most other British cities.

9 Urban problems: less economically developed countries

Rapid city growth has led to many problems. In many cities housing seems to be the most pressing problem with many people living in shanty towns. There are other related social and economic problems which are just as difficult to solve.

Industry

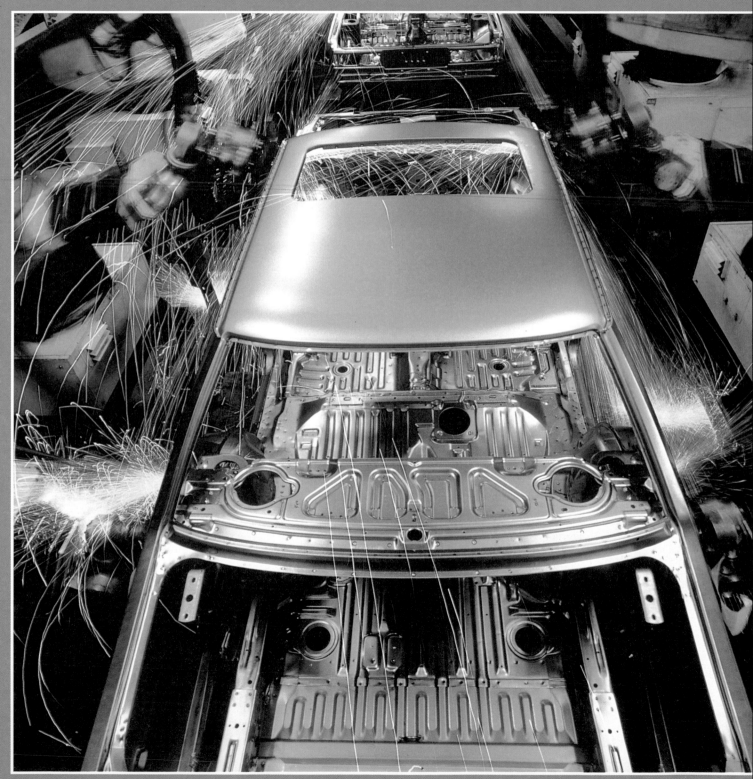

Robots welding car bodies on the assembly lines of the Mazda Car Plant, Hiroshima, Japan.

Types of work

The word 'industry' covers a range of activities which may involve making, supplying or delivering goods and services to a number of people.

Industries can be classified according to the types of jobs which people do; this is called **employment structure.** There are three main types, although with changes in technology, a fourth one can now be added (Source 1).

| Source 1 | Types of work |

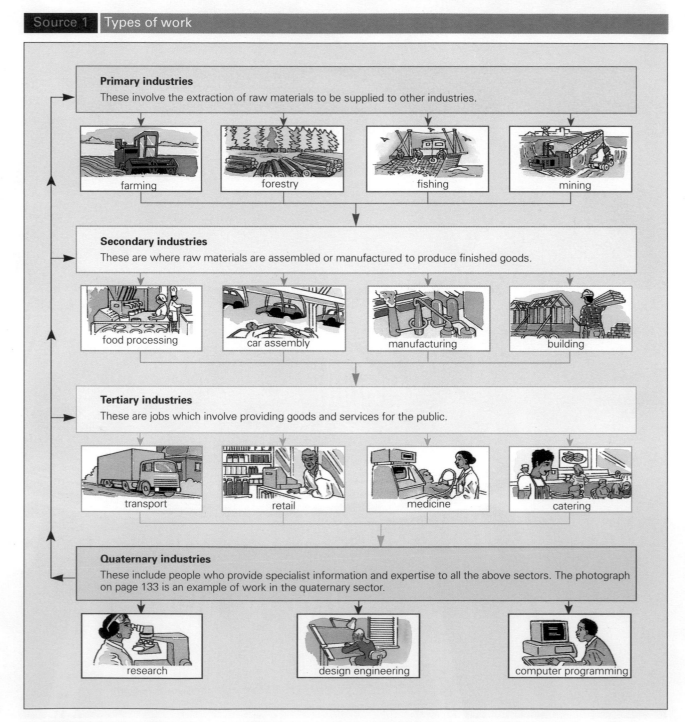

Primary industries
These involve the extraction of raw materials to be supplied to other industries.

farming forestry fishing mining

Secondary industries
These are where raw materials are assembled or manufactured to produce finished goods.

food processing car assembly manufacturing building

Tertiary industries
These are jobs which involve providing goods and services for the public.

transport retail medicine catering

Quaternary industries
These include people who provide specialist information and expertise to all the above sectors. The photograph on page 133 is an example of work in the quaternary sector.

research design engineering computer programming

Comparing employment structures

Employment structure can change over time and it also differs from country to country. The pie charts in Source 2 show the proportion of people working in three different sectors in Britain and Bangladesh. This information can also be used to compare levels of development between countries. The pie chart for Bangladesh shows that a higher proportion of the population work in primary industries like farming. By contrast a more economically developed country (MEDC) like Britain has a high proportion of people working in the tertiary sector.

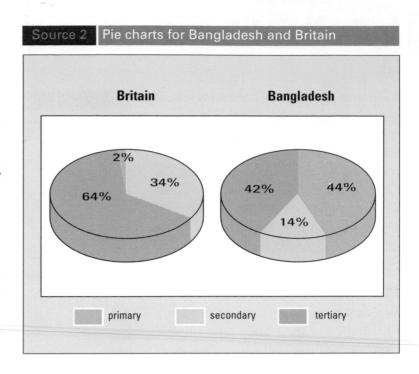

Source 2   Pie charts for Bangladesh and Britain

Britain   Bangladesh

primary   secondary   tertiary

Industry as a system

One way of describing how the manufacturing industry works is to view it as a system. A system is a way of organising an activity. It is made up of inputs, processes and outputs.

- **inputs** these are the raw materials that go into making a product
- **processes** these are the jobs or activities that take place in a factory
- **outputs** these are often the finished goods, which are sold to make a profit for the company.

The flow diagram below (Source 3) shows what the system might look like for a car factory. The feedback loop shows how some of the profits are reinvested in the business, ensuring that the industry continues to make money.

Source 3   A car factory system

| Inputs | → | Processes | → | Outputs |

Steel
Glass
Rubber
Paint
Plastics
Textiles
Tin
Iron ore

At the final stages the engine is placed in the car

Profits

Industrial location

Economic activities are not evenly spread around the United Kingdom. Some areas have high concentrations of industry – for example, Cambridge is an important centre for hi-tech industries (Source 1). Other areas, like the Scottish Highlands for example, have few industries. Different industries have specific needs or factors which influence their location. Some of these factors are outlined below.

Flat land Some industries, like car factories, need large areas of flat land. Often the cheapest and most suitable sites are on **greenfield locations** away from the city.

Raw materials Manufacturing industries like steelmaking rely on bulky raw materials, for example coal and limestone, which are expensive to transport. As a result many traditional **heavy industries** were located close to their raw materials.

Energy In the past it was important for factories to be close to power supplies, for example textile mills were built close to supplies of fast-flowing water. Today the widespread availability of electricity makes this less important.

Source 1	Industrial areas in the UK

0   150 km

N

Central Lowlands
• high-technology
• electronics

North-east
• cars
• offshore rigs
• chemicals

Belfast
• shipbuilding

Midlands
• car making
• engineering
• textiles

Barrow
• shipbuilding

Cambridge
• high-technology

Merseyside
• chemicals

South Wales
• steel
• electronics
• car components

East Anglia
• light industry

M4 corridor
• high-technology electronics

Solent
• chemicals

London
• commerce
• food processing

Labour force Industries that rely on a large workforce, like car production, tend to be found close to or within easy reach of cities where many of their workers and customers live. Source 2 shows another example of a **labour intensive** factory: clothing factories are often found in inner cities.

Markets Manufacturers do not like to be far from their markets as this increases costs. One reason why Sony decided to make televisions in Britain was to be nearer to its European markets.

Transport links Factories need to be located close to good transport links to ensure that the raw materials they need and the finished products they manufacture are moved with ease.

Source 2	An inner city clothing factory

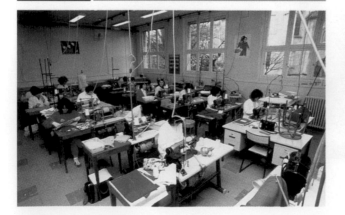

Source 3 — Assisted areas in the UK, 1993

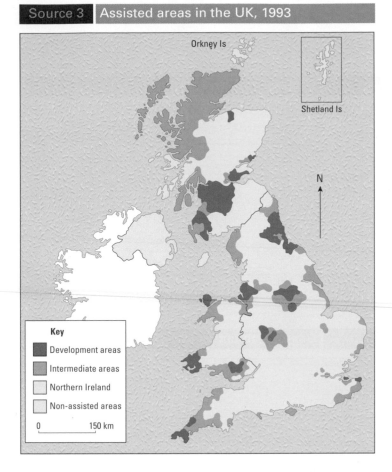

Orkney Is

Shetland Is

N

Key
- Development areas
- Intermediate areas
- Northern Ireland
- Non-assisted areas

0 ——— 150 km

What can governments do?

Where regions have lost industries or unemployment is high, then governments may provide money, or other forms of help to attract new investment. **Assisted areas** are regions which receive some form of aid (Source 3). Help may come in the form of:

- rent-free periods, grants and loans
- infrastructure: for example roads, water supplies and electricity
- retraining schemes – to provide labour with relevant skills
- enterprise zones – making it easier for firms to set up in inner city areas.

New jobs in new places

Some secondary activities can be grouped according to their location.

Heavy industries rely on bulky raw materials and tend to be found close to them, to reduce transport costs.

Light or **footloose industries** can locate almost anywhere, provided that communications are good. In the past, manufacturing industries were found close to their raw materials. Now, with developments in transport, industries do not have to be tied to a certain location. They can be footloose. Today many products are made on industrial estates (Source 4) located close to cities.

Highly specialised quaternary activities like research take place in **science parks** (see page 143).

In future it is believed that with the widespread use of computers, modems and the Internet, more and more people will be able to work from their own homes or even in small communities known as **tele-cottages**. Some such communities already exist in rural areas of South Wales.

Source 4 — Industrial estate

close to city for workers

purpose-built buildings

car parks

cheap land

close to roads

Industrial change

Workplaces rarely stay the same. The way goods and services are produced and delivered has changed dramatically over the last century. This has had a huge impact on people's lives and on the location of work in the United Kingdom.

One of the biggest changes has been the loss of jobs in the primary and secondary sectors (Source 1). Since the Second World War (1939–45) there has been a decline in the number of people working in mining and manufacturing. Some reasons for this include the following:

• Mechanisation and **automation** meant that fewer people were needed in factories.
• Many firms did not spend enough money on updating their factories.
• Competition from certain newly industrialised countries like South Korea and Taiwan, who can manufacture products more cheaply and efficiently.

As thousands of jobs disappeared it was the regions of traditional heavy industry, such as the North East, that suffered the most, as Source 2 shows.

The impact of change

Unemployment can have a devastating effect upon individuals, families and society at large. When one of the last shipyards on the Tyne closed, a newspaper reported some of the effects (Source 3).

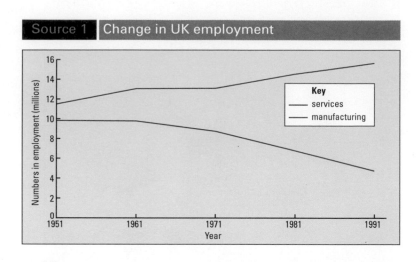

Source 1 — Change in UK employment

Source 2 — Unemployment by UK region

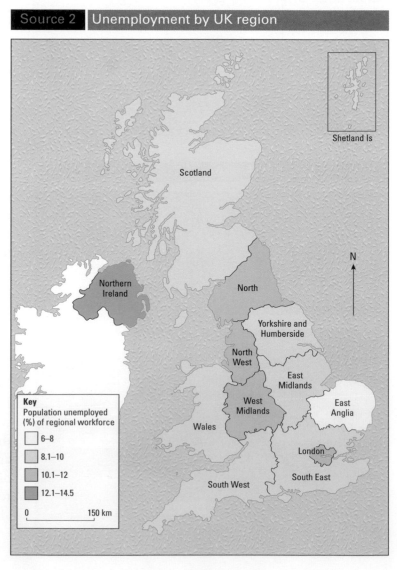

Other effects of industrial decline are that:

- people may lose their homes
- local shops close because people can't afford to use them
- families may break up.

Service industries

Not all areas of industry have been in decline over the last 100 years, for example many new jobs have been created in **service industries**. Service industries include activities as diverse as tourism, banking and transport. Much of the growth has been concentrated in urban areas, especially in southern Britain. Here, the importance of London as a financial centre has played an important role in attracting new jobs. Economic decline in the north and west and growth in the south have led to **regional inequalities**. However, in the late 1980s the technological revolution began to affect service industries and many jobs have been lost in sectors like banking as cash machines have replaced bank clerks (Source 4).

New jobs for old?

Areas of high unemployment were given assisted area status (see page 137) to attract new industry. This has led to a steady stream of inward investment by companies from the Far East like Sony and Toyota. The head of a Taiwanese firm opening a new TV factory in Scotland said his company was attracted to Britain for the following reasons:

- low labour costs
- there are few strikes – so industrial relations are good
- government help in the form of grants
- to be close to their European markets.

One drawback of the new jobs created is that many of the long-term unemployed do not have the skills to work in the new industries. While some people have been retrained, this has not been possible for all workers.

There has also been an increase in the number of **part-time jobs** which has attracted women into the workforce (Source 5). Part-time work often pays less and is less secure than full-time work. In future it is thought that people will no longer have a job for life. They will need to train and retrain throughout their careers, to keep pace with changes in the workplace.

| Source 3 | A Newspaper report, 1994 |

Decline and Decay

Inner city areas have pockets of unemployment reaching 50%. There are high levels of poverty, poor health, crime and vandalism, low educational achievement and low expectations.

| Source 4 | Machines like this cost jobs |

| Source 5 | Women play an active role in the workforce |

Global industry: the transnationals

One of the biggest changes in industry in the last 50 years has been the way the production of certain goods has become increasingly concentrated in the hands of a few large companies. Source 1 shows the names of a number of famous companies. What they all have in common is that they are all **transnational corporations** (TNCs).

A transnational corporation is a large company which has many factories or branch plants in a number of countries. Most transnationals are also involved in a range of different economic activities. Unilever is a good example of one such transnational corporation. Its headquarters are in London and Rotterdam: this is where the most important decisions about the company are made. However, Unilever, which owns many brand names from Bird's Eye fish fingers to Persil washing powder, operates in many different countries (Source 2).

Key
countries where Unilever owns (wholly or partially) operating companies

Many transnationals can control the whole production process, from raw materials to the finished product. For example where a product like a car is **assembled** or put together in a factory, many of the raw materials will have been gathered together from all over the world.

Source 3	The advantages and disadvantages of transnationals

Advantages	Disadvantages
• provide jobs in mines, factories and plantations	• profits may leave the country
• develop infrastructure, like roads and railways	• they may use cheap unskilled labour
• earn the host country foreign currency when goods are sold abroad	• they may close factories and move to somewhere more profitable
• invest in new technology	• use of technology may increase unemployment
• bring in professional skills	• may produce goods which are not appropriate to local needs
• develop trade links with other countries	• often have no regard for the local environment

Source 4	TNCs' investment in developing nations, 1991

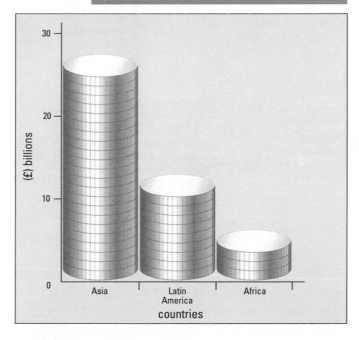

Source 5	Benetton in Namibia

As a result, transnational corporations are extremely powerful and as much as 70 per cent of world trade is the exchange of materials and goods between TNCs. Some of the profits made are so high that TNCs are often richer than many nations of the less economically developed world. It's not surprising then that many poorer countries are keen to attract transnational investment, but there are advantages and disadvantages which need to be weighed up carefully (Source 3).

Where does the money go?

Even though less economically developed countries (LEDCs) are keen to attract transnationals, three-quarters of all TNCs' investment goes to the more economically developed countries (MEDCs). In recent years some poorer nations have begun to make it easier for TNCs to set up branch plants in their countries. Source 4 shows that countries in Asia and Latin America have attracted more companies and investment than Africa.

Another sign of the power of transnationals is the way people from many different countries may use the same products. Levi jeans are worn by people all over the world, and Benetton's 'United Colours' advertising theme supported the idea that we are all global consumers as well as producers (Source 5).

Industrial change
South Wales

There was a time when the industrial landscape of Wales was littered with chimney stacks and smoke, signs that the region was dominated by heavy industry.

During the 1920s there were over a quarter of a million coal miners in South Wales. Today there are only around 1000. The number of miners and collieries has declined dramatically since then, as Source 1 shows.

Coal was a major source of fuel and helped provide the power needed for the Industrial Revolution. South Wales also had the raw materials needed to make steel: limestone, iron ore and coal (Source 1). Coal and steel were the two biggest industries in the region and part of their success was due to the fact that Britain still had an empire, which was a ready market for coal and steel.

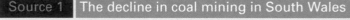

Source 1 — The decline in coal mining in South Wales

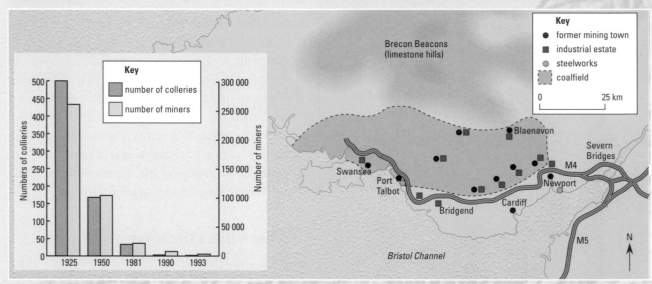

Source 2 — Big Pit in Blaenavon

Today coal mines are more likely to be tourist attractions, such as Big Pit in Blaenavon (Source 2), on the northern edge of the old coal field. The last British Coal owned mine closed in 1994, although a small number of privately run mines still operate. The two steelworks that remain are both found on the coast because they now rely on imported coal and iron ore.

Reasons for the decline in coal-mining included:

- Britain lost some of its markets for coal
- competition from Japan and South Korea
- all the easily worked coal seams were exhausted
- gas is now a major source of fuel, so coal is no longer in demand.

Unemployment in South Wales was above the national average for many years. This had a huge impact on smaller mining communities where the local pit would have been the only source of work.

Regenerating South Wales

In recent years, however, unemployment has fallen and South Wales has succeeded in **diversifying** by attracting a range of different industries. The Welsh Development Agency (WDA) was set up to help attract new investment into Wales. Parts of South Wales have also been given Enterprise Zone status. This means that new companies locating in the area do not have to pay local taxes, and receive help with planning. The work of the Welsh Development Agency and the Enterprise Zone have helped to change the industrial scene in South Wales.

As a result, many large industrial estates have emerged on the southern edge of the old coalfield where the road links are better. Grants and loans were given to new companies. This, combined with a pool of skilled workers, acted as a magnet for foreign firms like Sony, Bosch and Toyota, who have all set up factories in South Wales.

Source 3 | Imperial Park, South Wales

- **excellent road and rail links**
- **spacious parkland setting**
- **9140m^2 office space available**
- **close ties with Imperial College of Science and Technology**
- **future links with Cardiff University planned**
- **purpose-built accommodation**
- **support from Newport Borough Council and the Welsh Development Agency**

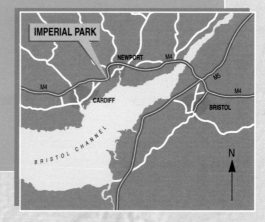

A science park: Imperial Park, Newport

In Newport in South Wales the WDA together with Newport Council have been keen to encourage the development of high-technology based industries. They achieved this by creating a science park named Imperial Park. This opened in 1994. Source 3 shows what it offers.

Here, good access, a scenic location and links with local universities are important locational factors. By 1996, there were eight companies operating in Imperial Park, specialising in food testing and software design. Imperial Park prides itself on being an extension of the M4 corridor, which is home to many science parks and hi-tech industries.

South Wales is a clear example of how a region which for so long specialised in a few industries can diversify. Today it plays host to manufacturing, service, high-technology and the tourist industry, with the signs of heavy industry fading fast.

A transnational corporation
Nike

Nike trainers (Source 1) are sold and worn throughout the world. Nike is a typical transnational corporation (TNC). Its headquarters are in the USA, where all the major decisions and research take place, yet its sports shoes are manufactured in many countries around the world.

Like many TNCs, Nike **subcontracts** or uses independently owned factories in different countries to produce its trainers. Often this takes place in less economically developed countries (LEDCs) where labour costs are low.

Nike's main activities are in south-east Asia, and up until recently it manufactured many of its trainers in South Korea. In the late 1980s labour costs in South Korea rose, so Nike decided to move production to Indonesia where costs were lower.

Source 1 | Where your money goes

cost to you
£53.00

wholesale price
£26.00

Where does the £26.00 go?

Transport £16.00

Materials £6.50

Administration £1.60

Labour £1.10

Sub-contractors' profit £0.80

The true price of trainers

Many of the workers in the Indonesian factories come from the surrounding countryside where they live in poverty. The conditions they move to are not much better. Some of the problems they face are:

- low wages and long hours
- industrial accidents
- no workers' rights – trade unions are illegal in Indonesia.

Where workers do complain or protest they can lose their jobs or in some cases 'disappear'.

The contractors say they cannot afford to pay the workers more and Nike says that it is difficult to control what is happening in individual factories. This means that in a nation where unemployment is high and employees can be easily replaced, workers will continue to be **exploited** (Source 2).

Source 2 | Many workers are exploited

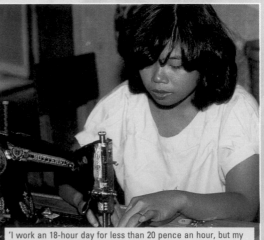

'I work an 18-hour day for less than 20 pence an hour, but my life in the countryside wasn't much better. There's not much we can do about it. If I lose my job there are plenty of other people to take my place.'

A newly industrialised country 8.7
South Korea

South Korea, Taiwan, Hong Kong and Singapore (Source 1) have one thing in common: they all have fast-growing economies. They have each undergone rapid economic change, which means they are **newly industrialised countries.**

What is remarkable about South Korea is that straight after the Second World War most of the population worked on farms, and industry was poorly developed. Given that it has few natural resources of its own, it is surprising that South Korea has one of the fastest growing economies in the world. Its Gross National Product is growing twice as fast as Britain's, as Source 2 shows.

The reasons for the economic miracle can be traced back to the 1950s when South Korea received cheap loans and technical help from the USA and other Western nations. From the 1960s onwards success has been achieved because of:

- a highly trained and dedicated workforce
- skilled management
- a determination to do well and export goods.

Today, South Korea earns most of its money from the export of manufactured goods. Hyundai is an example of a giant industrial corporation producing everything from micro-electronics to ships.

South Korea has become so successful that it now competes directly with countries like Britain. In fact Britain has become a favoured location for many South Korean companies. Samsung and Daewoo have both opened factories here in recent years (Source 3). By setting up branch plants in Britain, these large corporations are in a better position to sell their goods in the growing European market.

Source 1 | The NICs in south-east Asia

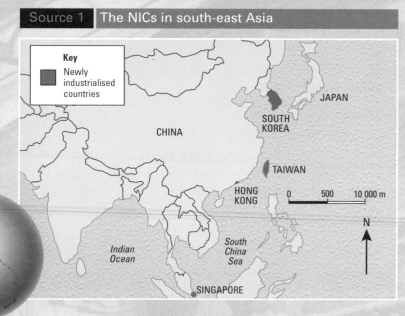

Key
Newly industrialised countries

JAPAN
SOUTH KOREA
CHINA
TAIWAN
HONG KONG
0 500 10 000 m
N
Indian Ocean
South China Sea
SINGAPORE

Source 2 | GNP growth rate: UK and South Korea

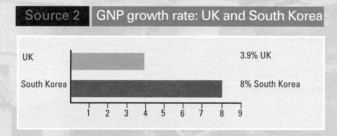

UK — 3.9% UK
South Korea — 8% South Korea
1 2 3 4 5 6 7 8 9

Source 3 | South Korean car made in the UK

Daewoo Nexia GLXi 5-Door

Industry in a less economically developed country
India

Despite a population of 900 million people and a wealth of natural resources, India remains one of the world's poorest nations.

Source 1 compares India with Britain. Despite its poverty, the Indian government has invested vast amounts of money trying to **industrialise** the country.

Planning for growth

After independence from Britain in 1947 India put into action a series of five-year plans. These were based on a communist model of development, called **import substitution**. This is where a country tries to produce all the goods it needs so it does not have to import products from other countries. Source 2 summarises what the plans tried to achieve.

Source 1 India compared with the UK

	UK	India
Area (in km²)	241 595	3 287 590
Population (in millions)	58.4	882.6
Population density (per km²)	241	263
Natural increase (%)	0.2	2.1
Life expectancy (years)	76	60
GNP per capita (US $)	17 760	330

Source 2 India's five-year plans

Plan	1–3	20% 4	5–9
Years	1951–66	1969–74	1979–1990
Aims	Develop heavy industry	Develop rural area	Develop infrastructure
Example	Damodar Valley natural resources like coal, ore and bauxite used to develop heavy industry	the green revolution investment in high yielding seeds	increase power supplies improve irrigation new roads and railways

Source 3 India's main industrial regions

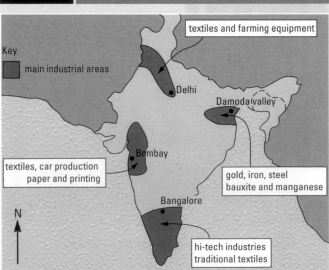

A great deal of money was spent on developing manufacturing industries. Source 3 shows some of the main regions which emerged. While heavy industry was concentrated in the north-east in the Damodar Valley, newer hi-tech industries were being encouraged in cities like Bangalore further south. Despite these plans, Indian industries continued to face a number of problems.

- Many areas suffered power shortages.
- India continued to import more than it exported – this led to **trade deficits**. India especially relied on oil. When prices rose rapidly in the 1970s this had a serious effect on Indian industry.
- Poor transport links made it hard to develop industry in more remote regions.
- Corruption and inefficiency led to waste.

For almost 50 years the Indian government supported and developed large-scale manufacturing. However, smaller, privately run firms are found across India, producing goods for a local market, but many of them are limited in what they can sell because people are too poor to afford consumer goods.

Source 4	Children often work in the informal sector

The informal sector

Unemployment is a huge problem in India, so people will turn their hand to a variety of activities in order to make a living. These might range from shoeshining to selling scrap metal. These are all examples of work in the informal sector. This type of work is characterised by insecurity, no taxes are paid and often workers receive 'cash in hand' payment. It is difficult to estimate how many people work in this sector because informal activities are illegal (Source 4).

Source 5	Information Technology Park, Bangalore

The main features of the Information Technology Park are the following.

- Space for offices, shops, luxury homes and parks.
- It is 18 km east of Bangalore and 20 minutes away from the airport.
- State-of-the-art modern buildings, power supply and communications.
- It is designed for technology oriented companies
- A landscaped park-like environment
- It is India's first science park.

A new future

Since the early 1990s the Indian government's approach to industry has changed. It is now keen to encourage foreign companies to open factories in India. It especially wants to develop hi-tech industries. One way forward is to create technology or science parks (Source 5).

Activities

1 Write a sentence to explain the meaning of the following terms: employment structure; greenfield location; assisted area; transnational corporation.

2 List five examples of jobs in the primary, secondary, tertiary and quaternary sectors in a copy of the table below:

Primary	Secondary	Tertiary	Quaternary

3 Study Source 1 below.

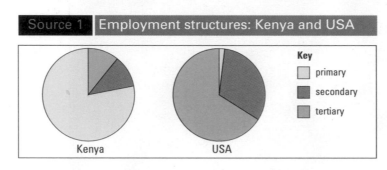

Source 1 Employment structures: Kenya and USA

Key
- primary
- secondary
- tertiary

Kenya   USA

a What is the percentage of people employed in primary industry in Kenya?

b What is the percentage of people employed in tertiary industry in the USA?

4 a Use the following information to construct your own pie chart for Brazil:
   Primary   30%   Secondary   22%   Tertiary   48%
   b Find out what the employment structure of the UK is (Source 2, page 135). Write a few sentences to compare it with Brazil, Kenya and the USA.

5 How does the employment structure of a less economically developed country differ from that of a more economically developed country?

6 a What is a transnational corporation?
   b Write down the names of some transnationals.
   c Research task – use the library/encyclopaedia/CD-Rom to write a report on a transnational corporation. Use the following headings:
   • Company history
   • Products/brand names
   • For one manufacturing industry complete a systems diagram.
   • Location throughout the world
   • Impact on countries the company operates in.

7 Cardiff is keen to attract the kind of high-tech industry featured on page 133.
   You work for the Welsh Development Agency – use the information from pages 142 and 143 and Sources 2, 3, 4 and 5 below to design a poster to attract new companies into your region. The following headings may help.

   • Skilled work force
   • Good transport links
   • Government incentives
   • Purpose built industrial estates
   • Close links with London and other major centres

Source 2 Table of rail distances from Cardiff

Bristol	37 minutes
London	1hr 47 minutes
Birmingham	1hr 54 minutes
Southampton	2hrs 32 minutes
Manchester	3hrs 24 minutes
Sheffield	3hrs 28 minutes

Source 3 Map of drivetime isochrones from Cardiff

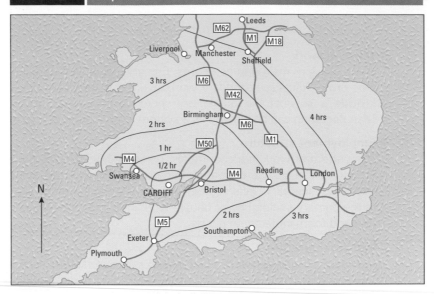

Source 4 | Table showing quality of life in British cities

Quality of Life
How British Cities Rank

City	Rank
Edinburgh	1
CARDIFF	**4**
Reading	7
Oxford	11
Portsmouth	14
Bristol	19
Bournemouth	26
Manchester	30
London	34
Birmingham	38

Source 5 | Cardiff: a capital city

'Cardiff is a revelation; a capital city of 280 000 people, living within 15 minutes of an elegant and modern city centre. It offers all the facilities you would usually find in much larger cities. The redevelopment of Cardiff Bay is one of the most ambitious regeneration projects ever seen in Europe to date.'

8 Write an account of the industrial profile of an area in the UK that you have studied. Describe the area's principal industries. Explain how the area's industries compare with those in South Wales.

1 Types of work

There are four main groups of jobs: primary, secondary, tertiary and quaternary. Primary jobs are extractive; secondary work involves manufacturing products; tertiary workers provide a service; the quaternary sector is concerned with knowledge-based work. Manufacturing can be viewed as a system, with inputs, processes and outputs.

2 Employment structure

The pattern of work in a country can be seen in its employment structure. Employment structures can change over time. In more economically developed countries, the tertiary sector dominates. In less economically developed countries like India more people work in the primary sector. Fewer people work in the secondary sector, because there is less demand for manufactured goods.

3 Industrial location

Industrial location depends on a complex range of factors. Heavy industries rely on bulky raw materials and so are found close to their raw materials. Light industries are footloose: many are found on industrial estates.

Governments often encourage industries to locate in depressed regions. They do this by offering a variety of incentives – some of them financial.

4 Industrial change

Developments in technology and competition from abroad have led to heavy job losses in British industry. There are fewer secure jobs today and workers often need to have more than one skill.

South Wales is a region that has suffered from high unemployment and social problems caused by industrial change. The coal mining industry has suffered a major decline and this has led to high levels of unemployment. Parts of the region have succeeded in attracting new investment, which has brought new jobs. The Welsh Development Agency (WDA) has helped to attract companies from other parts of the UK as well as from overseas.

5 Global industry: the transnationals

An increasing number of goods and services are provided by transnational corporations. Transnationals are very powerful and many people depend on them to make a living. Nike is an example of a transnational corporation. Its headquarters are in the USA, but it chooses to manufacture goods in countries throughout the world where wage costs are low.

6 Newly industrialised countries

Some countries have developed their manufacturing sector very quickly. These countries, like South Korea, Hong Kong and Taiwan, are called newly industrialised countries (NICs). Much of the industrial output of NICs is exported. Some NICs are now locating manufacturing plants in other countries.

Farming as an industry

Farming can sculpt a different landscape

Types of farming

People need to grow food in order to live. There are many different ways of grouping or classifying farming activities. In Britain, farmers grow crops and rear animals for sale. This is called **commercial farming**. In less economically developed countries, many farmers only grow enough to feed their families. This is called **subsistence farming**.

Market gardens in the Netherlands

Farms can also be grouped according to the way farmers use their land. Farming can be:

- **intensive** this involves spending a lot of time and money on the farmland to produce high yields, an example is market gardening (Source 1).
- **extensive** this is where farmers use large areas of land to rear animals and produce crops (see page 151). Less machinery and labour is needed than in intensive farms. An example is ranching.

Sedentary farming is when farmers stay in one place to grow their crops. This can be contrasted with **shifting cultivation** and **nomadic herding**, where people move to find fertile or good grazing land.

Commercial farming

In more economically developed countries (MEDCs) like Britain, most farming is commercial. The main types are as shown in the table below.

Type	Activity
Arable	the growing of crops and cereals, such as wheat
Pastoral	livestock such as beef, cattle, pigs and poultry are reared
Hill farming	sheep are kept for their meat and wool
Mixed farming	a combination of arable and pastoral farming

In less economically developed countries (LEDCs), big companies such as Brooke Bond own large estates where one crop is grown. These estates are called **plantations** and the system of growing only one crop is known as **monoculture**. Plantation crops include tea, sugar, rubber and cocoa.

The dry grasslands of North and South America are used for **ranching**. Cattle and sheep are reared on large farms. This is large-scale pastoral activity.

Subsistence farming

Many farmers in less economically developed countries grow crops or rear animals for their own use (Source 2).

Subsistence farmers use little machinery

Shifting cultivation

Many people who live in rainforests or the savanna clear their land to grow crops for a number of years. When the soil is no longer fertile the farmers move on to a fresh plot of land. This is called **shifting cultivation**. Most subsistence farmers grow a variety of cereals and vegetables. If they grow more than they need, it can be sold locally.

Nomadic herding

In places where there is no reliable source of water the farmers are nomadic. Nomads keep livestock and move from one place to another in search of water and fresh pasture. They roam over large areas of land and often share their grazing land with others. The Masai of Kenya are an example of a nomadic people. Nomads use few resources.

| Source 3 | Types of farming |

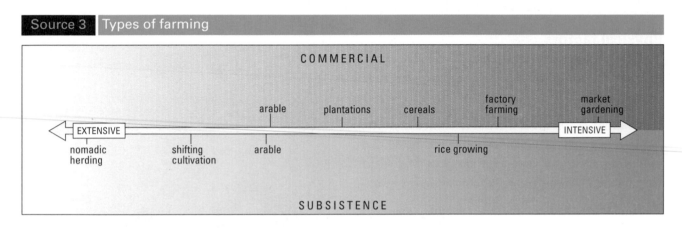

| Source 4 | A farm system |

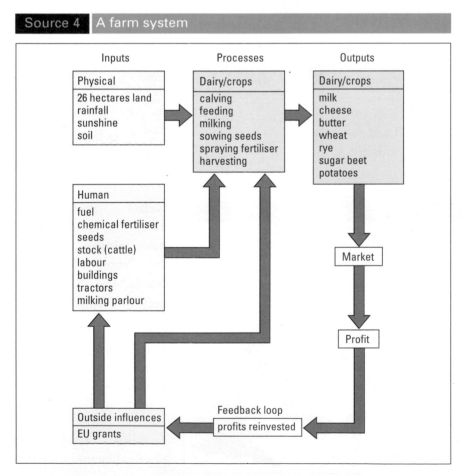

The farming system

One way of looking at farms is to view them as a system. All systems have these:

Inputs are what goes into the system, such as cows, money, or seeds. Processes might include activities such as milking cattle and sowing seeds. Outputs are the products of the system, for example milk or crops. Source 4 is an example of a farm system for a mixed farm in Devon.

Factors affecting farming

The distribution of farming types in Britain is influenced by physical and human factors. Source 1 reveals the pattern of farming. To understand why farming types are distributed in this way, we shall first look at the physical geography of the British Isles.

Physical factors

The physical factors are what a crop needs in order to grow. Deciding which crops can be grown in an area depends on the following five physical factors.

Rainfall all crops need a reliable source of water. Some crops such as wheat do not need more than 600 millimetres per year. This explains why wheat is grown in the south-east where rainfall is low.

Temperature most crops cannot grow if temperatures regularly fall below 4°C. This is one reason why fruit and vegetables tend to be grown in the south-east.

Sunshine hours the more sun that crops receive the more likely they are to ripen quickly.

Soil type farmers find that crops grow best on free-draining soils; these let water through and so do not become waterlogged. Deep fertile soils are best for growing crops.

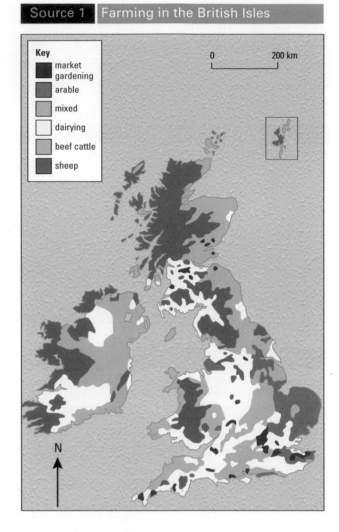

Source 1 Farming in the British Isles

Key
- market gardening
- arable
- mixed
- dairying
- beef cattle
- sheep

0   200 km

N

Relief mountainous areas tend to be cold and have slopes that are too steep for farm machinery. Sheep are kept in hilly, wet areas.

Source 2 shows how relief, rainfall and the number of sunshine hours vary from one place to another. There is clearly a link between farming type and physical factors.

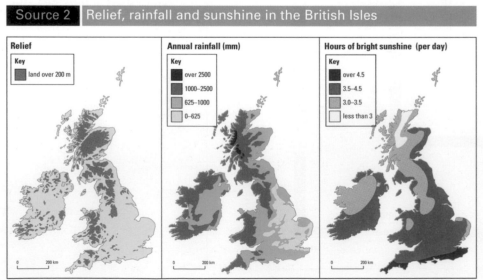

Source 2 Relief, rainfall and sunshine in the British Isles

Relief

Key
- land over 200 m

Annual rainfall (mm)

Key
- over 2500
- 1000–2500
- 625–1000
- 0–625

Hours of bright sunshine (per day)

Key
- over 4.5
- 3.5–4.5
- 3.0–3.5
- less than 3

0   200 km   0   200 km   0   200 km

Human factors

While physical geography greatly influences how farmers use their land, farmers also need to consider human factors. Decisions taken are based on a farmer's perceptions of what is believed will be 'best'. Of course this may change with age and experience. Making decisions can be incredibly complex – Source 3 illustrates some of the different choices a farmer needs to consider.

Source 3	Some food for thought

Source 4	The EU encourages the growth of oil-seed rape

The amount of **capital** a farmer has will affect whether machinery can be bought or how many workers can be paid. If a farm is going to make a profit, then it must have a **market** for its goods. Some farmers have contracts with large supermarkets. For example, Sainsbury's obtains some of its apples from the market gardens of Kent. The European Union's **Common Agricultural Policy** (CAP) has also had an impact on many farmers in Britain.

The Common Agricultural Policy (CAP)

Following the formation of the European Union in 1956, the Common Agricultural Policy (CAP) was developed. One of its aims was to prevent food shortages from occurring. In order to do this the EU needed to ensure that farmers had a good standard of living and so did not leave the land.

The EU provides farmers with **subsidies** (that is, money) to grow certain crops such as oil-seed rape (Source 4). They make it harder for countries outside the EU to sell their products in Europe by adding a **tariff** (tax) to the imported foods. The effect of these policies is described on page 157.

Agriculture in change

Images of the British countryside may give the impression that nothing changes, yet patterns in the landscape are the result of many upheavals in farming. Source 1 shows a typical 1990s landscape; a similar view in the 1940s would have been very different.

During the last 50 years farming has become an important industry. Below are some of the major changes.

Source 1 — A typical rural landscape in the 1990s

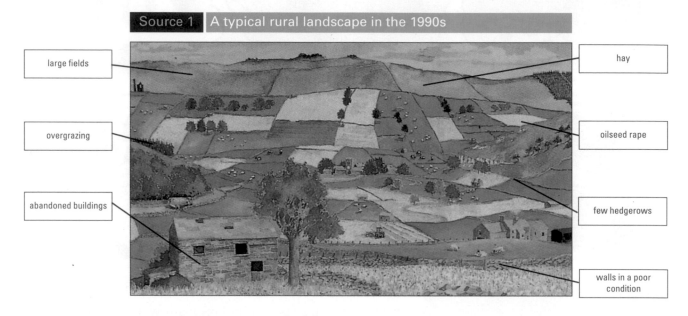

large fields

overgrazing

abandoned buildings

hay

oilseed rape

few hedgerows

walls in a poor condition

Source 2 — Job losses on farms

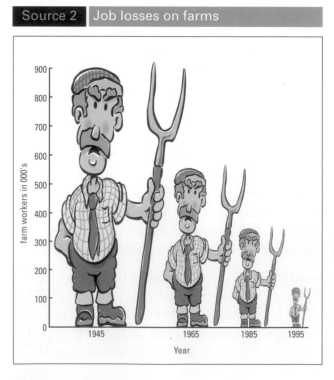

farm workers in 000's

Year

Job losses Since the Second World War many people have left the land (Source 2). In part this is because many jobs were replaced by machines.

Mechanisation In 1944 there were 168 000 tractors. By the 1990s this figure had increased to 600 000. To make effective use of the machinery, fields need to be large. This has resulted in the removal of hedgerows and, in some cases, small farms have merged or **amalgamated**.

Factory farming Most people buy their food at supermarkets. Supermarkets sell such large quantities of food that they must buy stock in bulk. Many farmers have large contracts with supermarket chains and freezer companies. This has encouraged farms to amalgamate.

Pesticides and fertilisers The growing use of chemical fertilisers and pesticides has led to an increase in yields.

Our changing countryside

Britain has lost thousands of kilometres of hedgerows in the last 40 years (Source 3), and as a result many birds and small animals have lost their homes. Hedgerows are also used as windbreaks, and their removal makes the soil vulnerable to soil erosion. This has been greatest on arable farms in East Anglia where large fields are common.

The effects of the Common Agricultural Policy (CAP)

The European Union has encouraged farmers to use their land more intensively. It bought up surplus produce when farmers couldn't sell their crops. This led to the creation of huge food mountains. This food was going to waste and costs of storing it were high, so the CAP was reformed. From 1992 farmers who received grants from the EU had to take 20 per cent of their arable land out of production: this is called **set aside.**

The farming industry has been hard hit by these changes and many farmers have had to **diversify.** It is estimated that in 1991 almost 40 per cent of farmers were reliant on non-agricultural activities. These include the following:

- **Leisure** Farms with good access to urban areas have found it profitable to open their farms to the public. Many have applied for golf courses to be developed on their land.

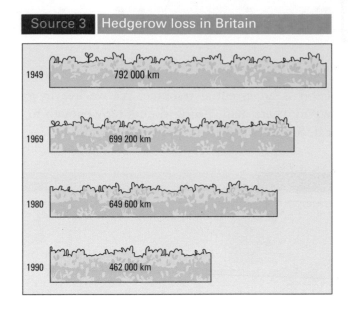

| Source 3 | Hedgerow loss in Britain |

1949 — 792 000 km
1969 — 699 200 km
1980 — 649 600 km
1990 — 462 000 km

| Source 4 | People protesting over the export of live animals |

- **Tourism** Farms in scenic locations such as the Lake District are increasingly offering bed and breakfast accommodation to tourists.
- **Conifer plantations** Under the Farm Woodland Scheme farmers receive a grant to plant conifers. The growing number of conifers is matched by a huge loss of broad-leaved woodlands.
- **Conservation** Farmers have been encouraged to protect their environment by agreeing to register their land as **Environmentally Sensitive Areas (ESAs).** Under this scheme farmers receive a payment if they agree to:

  - limit their use of fertilisers
  - restore drystone walls
  - reduce the number of animals they keep.

Future trends

With growing public concern about the environment and animal welfare, changes in farming are likely to continue (Source 4). Some people believe that intensive farming methods can affect human health. For example, it is thought that the antibiotics added to chicken feed can lead to salmonella poisoning. **Organic farming** attempts to avoid the use of pesticides, fertilisers and antibiotics. The government now offers grants to farmers wishing to switch to organic methods.

Farming and famine

Food is an essential resource, yet we live in a world where many people do not have enough to eat. Source 1 shows the parts of the world at risk from **famine**. All the areas shown are in less economically developed countries (LEDCs).

Famine areas of the world

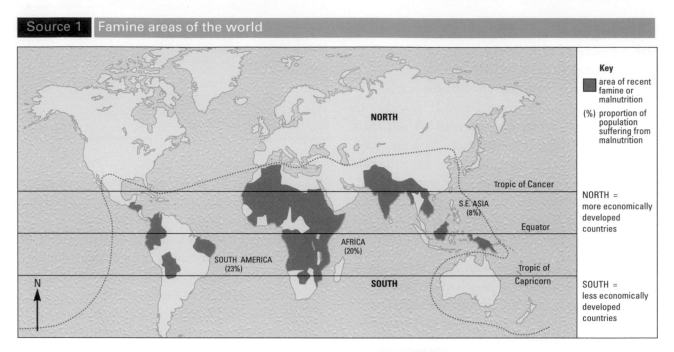

Key

area of recent famine or malnutrition

(%) proportion of population suffering from malnutrition

NORTH = more economically developed countries

SOUTH = less economically developed countries

NORTH

Tropic of Cancer

S.E. ASIA (8%)

Equator

AFRICA (20%)

SOUTH AMERICA (23%)

Tropic of Capricorn

SOUTH

N

It is estimated that on average an adult needs a balanced diet providing about 2300 Calories per day. In the more economically developed countries (MEDCs), Calorie consumption is high and the number of overweight people is increasing. This can lead to heart disease and strokes. By contrast, in many African nations people only manage to consume

Source 2 Daily calorie supply

80 per cent of this amount (Source 2). A lack of Calories and the right vitamins can cause **malnutrition**, making people weak and sick.

The result of many illnesses is that people become too weak to work. This contributes to the 'circle of hunger' (Source 3), from which it is difficult to escape.

Source 3 The circle of hunger

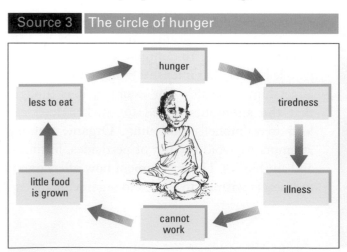

hunger

tiredness

less to eat

illness

little food is grown

cannot work

The causes of famine

Some people believe that famines are a result of people's laziness or ignorance. The fact is that the causes are complex and can include any one or more of the following:

Drought When the rains fail, harvests can be destroyed and farmers are left without food.

Desertification The removal of trees (deforestation) and overgrazing result in land that is easily eroded and so turns to desert and becomes unproductive.

War Wars can destroy farming as people leave the land to fight or escape, and money is spent on weapons rather than on agriculture. Source 4 tells what happened to one family during the war in Somalia in 1992.

Poverty Landless people do not have land to farm on.

Trade LEDCs get poor prices for the cash crops which they export, yet they pay a high price for manufactured goods which they import from the developed world.

International debt LEDCs owe money to the MEDCs. Many countries have such a huge debt that most of their income goes towards paying off interest on their loans. This leaves little to spend on farming.

What can be done?

There are a variety of actions that people can take to help farmers in the developing world (see Source 5).

Source 4 Famine as a result of war

Famine in Somalia

The drought affected Abdi Husein's farm near Bardera in Somalia. When it passed he was able to grow corn, tomatoes and olives. But then war reached his village and things got worse.

'I had plenty stored, but they grabbed all my food and took all my animals and personal belongings', said Husein from his hospital bed.

With his wife, daughter and six sons, Husein made his way to Doblei, the nearest town, eating wild fruits and leaves and gnawing on animal skins. The children died, some from gunfire during the battle, some from hunger.

In Doblei, Husein became more ill, before they heard a rumour that emergency food supplies were on their way.

Source 5 'Fairtrade' means a fairer price

We could give aid, but this might only help people in the short term. People might become too dependent on aid in the long term.

We need to improve the way food is produced. Farmers ought to use more intensive methods such as machinery, fertilisers and pesticides.

Farmers should be given their own land. Small loans would help them buy inexpensive tools, allowing them to use their own knowledge and skills.

Farmers should be given a fair price for their crops. Some companies that do this use the 'Fairtrade' mark. Maya Gold, which is an organic chocolate from Belize, tries to guarantee that peasant farmers are not exploited.

Fairtrade
Guarantees
a better deal
for Third World
Producers

GREEN & BLACK'S
MAYA GOLD
ORGANIC DARK CHOCOLATE
From cocoa beans *forest-grown* in the Maya Moutains of Belize - with orange and spice.

20g
0.7OZ

159

Arable farming
East Anglia

One region specialising in arable farming is East Anglia. The Ryston Estate is situated on the flat **fenlands** north of Ely. The Fens are areas of land that have been **reclaimed** from the sea. As a result the soils are deep and fertile.

The dry climate, with less than 650 millimetres of rainfall per year, and warm summers with an average temperature of 21°C make this an ideal region for growing crops. During the winter, frosts help to kill off disease and break up the soil, making it easier to plough. The Ryston Estate is typical of many farms in this region (Sources 1 and 2).

The main crop is wheat, which is sold directly to local mills to make animal feed. Sugar beet is another major source of income and is sold to the Wissington sugar beet factory. The linseed, beans and potatoes go to the local market.

Source 1 Farm file: Ryston Estate

FARM FILE

Name:
Ryston Estate

Ryston Estate

Location:
Downham Market, Norfolk

Size:
539 ha

Soil type:
Fen peat, clay and loam, which are fertile yet free draining

Workforce:
4 full-time, 2 part-time

Machinery:
5 tractors, 1 combine harvester and trailer, sorters and sprayers

Land use:

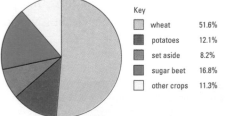

Key	
wheat	51.6%
potatoes	12.1%
set aside	8.2%
sugar beet	16.8%
other crops	11.3%

Source 2 OS map showing Ryston estate

©Crown copyright

0 ___ 1 km

The farm also receives **subsidies** from the European Union, without which the farm would not make a profit. In recent years the farmer has been encouraged to set aside some of his land and he currently receives a subsidy of £11 000 not to use 32 hectares of land.

Where rainfall is high and slopes are too rugged to grow crops then the land tends to be used for grazing sheep. This is known as **hill farming**. Hill farmers make a living by selling wool and selling some of their livestock for meat. In the United Kingdom most hill farming takes place in the highlands of the north and west. Hill farms cover large areas of land and need little machinery or labour. This makes hill farming

| Source 1 | A hill farm in the Lake District |

ALLOTMENT
grazing land surrounded by stone walls

HIGH FELL
rough grazing land

INBYE
grazing land close to the farmhouse

| Source 2 | Farm file: Lowther Estate |

FARM FILE

Lowther Estate

Name:
Lowther Estate
Location:
Hawes Water, Cumbria
Livestock: 1500 ewes and 55 cattle
Workforce: 3 full-time and some part-time help at lambing

one of the most extensive forms of farming in Britain. Sources 1 and 2 show the main features of a hill farm in the Lake District.

In recent years hill farmers have faced many problems, and in the Lake District alone almost a third of all farmers left the land in the 1980s to look for jobs elsewhere. It is difficult to make a living from hill farming as the price of sheep and their fleeces has fallen, while costs have risen. Even though hill farmers receive **subsidies** from the government, often it is not enough to make their work profitable. Some farmers in Cumbria believe they will be the last generation of hill farmers (Source 3). One hill farmer said: 'At the moment my son has no interest in farming and I don't think he will go into it. Children look round, see the effort we put in and think there are easier and more pleasant ways of making a living.'

Those hill farms which remain have had to diversify, and in the Lake District many of them have turned to tourism. Some now offer bed and breakfast facilities, farm tours and pony trekking in addition to their farming work. The income from tourists helps to keep the farms going.

| Source 3 | A hill farmer in Cumbria |

Rice for subsistence
India

There can be no doubt that rice is a major crop, given that it feeds one-third of the world's population. The main rice growing areas of the world are the nations of south-east Asia, including India. Here, rice is grown mainly for **subsistence** and what little is left is sold.

Source 2 | Rice growing areas of India

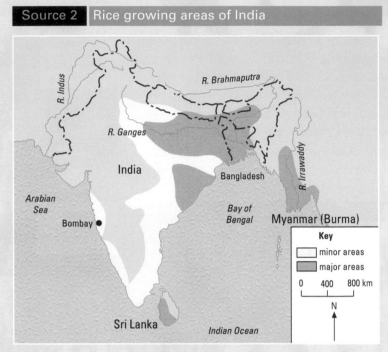

Source 1 | Climate graph for Bombay

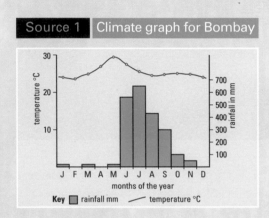

India offers the perfect type of climate for rice as temperatures do not fall below 21°C throughout the year (Source 1) and there is a long wet season, known as the **monsoon**. The monsoon arrives in May and ends in November. The monsoon winds pick up their moisture over the oceans. The monsoon is then followed by a dry spell which allows the rice to ripen and for harvesting to take place (Source 3).

Rice is grown in flooded fields known as **paddy fields** (Source 4). Where the slopes are too steep then **terraces** are cut into the hillsides. Rice requires a great deal of the farmer's time and attention and it can be grown in small plots of land. This makes it an intensive form of farming.

Source 3 | The rice farmer's year

Months	Farming activities
January	Farmer ploughs lowland fields. Plants peas, beans and lentils
February	Tends crops, weeds fields
March	Harvests crops
April	Non-farming jobs completed
May	Prepares rice seed bed, weeds, adds ash and manure to the fields. Waits for the rains, then sows seeds
June	Weeds fields
July	Ploughs in manure
August	Rice plants are moved to another field and are planted 25 cm apart
September	Continues to weed and add manure
October	Plants begin to flower
November	Rice ripens
December	Harvesting and threshing

Source 4 | A paddy field in India

Sowing the seeds of change

Traditional varieties of rice meant that there simply wasn't enough food to go round. As the population of the south-east Asian countries grew rapidly, food could not be grown fast enough. In 1959 the International Rice Research Institute (IRRI) was set up in the Philippines to look at how rice yields could be increased.

Researchers cross-bred two plants: a semi-dwarf plant from China with a strong, tall Indonesian plant. The result was a sturdy, short plant called IR8. How it compared with the traditional variety is shown in Source 5.

Source 5 | Comparing old and new rice plants

Old plant		New plant
grows rapidly		shorter, stronger plant
tall plant, can fall over easily		can be planted close together, needs little space
needs to be planted far apart		needs fertiliser and pesticides
5 months' growing season		4 months' growing season
average yield 1.5 tonnes per ha		average yield 5.0 tonnes per ha

New plants like IR8 proved to be a success because much more food could be produced. However, they made many demands on farmers. Expensive fertilisers and pesticides were needed and they required much more irrigation. Large-scale irrigation projects meant many small farmers lost their homes. The result has been that the rich have benefited while poor farmers could not afford to grow the new crop.

Plants like IR8 also attracted far more pests than the traditional varieties, and despite the many changes that have been made to IR8, this still remains a problem.

Nomadic farming
the Fulani

Climate plays an important role in the way land is used, especially in the Sahel. The Sahel is the main semi-desert area of Africa on the southern edge of the Sahara (Source 1). Here temperatures are hot for much of the year and there is a marked seasonal drought as Source 2 shows.

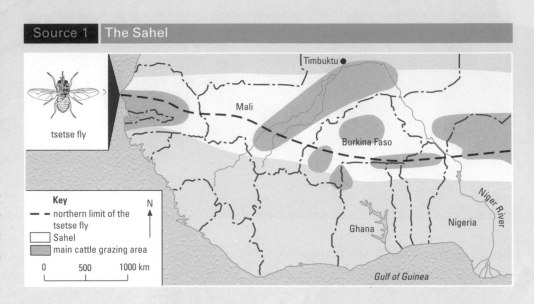

Source 1 The Sahel

tsetse fly

Key
- – – northern limit of the tsetse fly
- ▢ Sahel
- ▨ main cattle grazing area

0   500   1000 km

N

Timbuktu
Mali
Burkina Faso
Ghana
Nigeria
Niger River
Gulf of Guinea

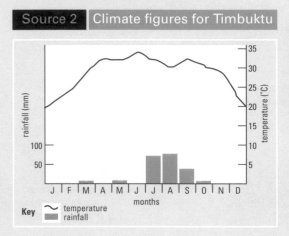

Source 2 Climate figures for Timbuktu

Key ∼ temperature ▨ rainfall

Source 3 Nomads

A lack of reliable rainfall makes it difficult for farmers to grow crops and explains why many people are forced to move from their land. These wanderers are called nomads.

The Fulani tribe in Mali move south during the dry season through Burkina and into Ghana. They stop at markets along their journey, where they trade some of their animals and milk for foodstuffs like grain. When the rains arrive in the south the nomads begin to move back to their homeland. They are driven away by the tsetse fly which brings disease to their livestock. Seasonal movement of grazing animals is called **transhumance**.

When nomads are forced to settle down, this can have serious consequences. The Fulani have traditionally grazed their cattle near the inland delta of the Niger River. The tribes took turns to graze cattle, so there was enough land to go round. When the government bought the land in the 1960s the Fulani's system was abandoned. Many tribespeople felt they had been cheated of their land, and so they increased the size of their herds and were forced to graze wherever they could.

This scheme resulted in the removal of vegetation through **overgrazing**. In time, **desertification** may take place and in the long term the land becomes useless. (See also page 87.)

Small-scale farming projects can often be just as effective as, and cause less damage to the environment than large-scale activities. **Appropriate technology** uses the skills of local people to find the best ways of improving their farming.

Intermediate Technology is an international development agency which works with people in rural communities in Kenya, Sudan, Zimbabwe, Sri Lanka, Bangladesh and Peru. It works with peasant farmers called *campesinos* in Peru.

Farmers in the highly populated, dry, western area of Peru are dependent on irrigation to grow crops. In recent years poor rains in the sierra mountains have reduced irrigation and water flows, leading to poor harvests. In the Ica valley (Source 1) this situation is made worse by rapid population growth caused by the migration of people from the drought-stricken sierra. Farmers in the valley depend on irrigation and either draw their water from the River Ica or the Choclocaya Dam in the upper reaches of the river, by way of La Archivana irrigation canal.

However, the way water has been managed favours richer farmers who produce cash crops for export, leaving the *campesinos* with little water for their land.

The aim of Intermediate Technology is to help organise the small farmers so that they can have a fair share of the water:

- farmers now have better access to information about their water rights and are helped to defend their interests through improved organisation
- technical support is also given and the *campesinos* are

being helped to rebuild some of their traditional technologies, like the wooden irrigation gates shown in Source 2.

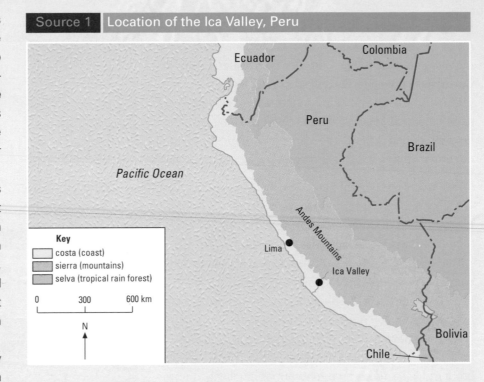

Source 1 Location of the Ica Valley, Peru

Key
- costa (coast)
- sierra (mountains)
- selva (tropical rain forest)

0   300   600 km

N

Colombia
Ecuador
Peru
Brazil
Pacific Ocean
Andes Mountains
Lima
Ica Valley
Bolivia
Chile

Source 2 Traditional methods of irrigation

Irrigated farming
California

It's hard to imagine how a desert can be one of the most productive areas of the USA. However, with money and technology the Central Valley desert in California is now a fertile agricultural region.

Much of California has a Mediterranean climate and, as Source 1 shows, this means there is a long summer drought during which little can grow. Farmers in the region faced two specific problems.

1 The Rivers Sacramento and San Joaquin did not supply enough water to **irrigate** the land.

2 Most of the rain fell in the northern part of the valley, yet the most fertile land was in the south.

The Central Valley Project was developed to help distribute water in California more effectively. It is a large irrigation project. Source 2 shows how dams were built in the upper reaches of the main rivers to store water. A series of canals connect these dams (Source 3) to the dry valleys 500 km further south. Water is then brought to the fields by a network of pipelines, sprays and sprinklers.

The cost of the scheme was so high that the land has to be farmed intensively. Only crops which have a high yield and value are grown, such as vines, vegetables and citrus fruits (oranges and lemons). Large-scale intensive commercial farming of this type is called **agribusiness**.

Large schemes like the Central Valley Project are controversial. They have advantages and disadvantages as the table below shows.

Advantages	Disadvantages
Crops can be grown.	Cost – farmers pay a high price for the water. This benefits rich Californian farmers.
Dams can be used for tourism.	
Dams can provide hydro electric power.	Salts are left behind when water evaporates. This poisons the land.
Industry is attracted to cheap sources of power.	
	Dams will silt up in time.

Source 1 Climate in the San Joaquin Valley

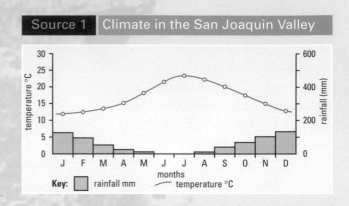

Key: □ rainfall mm   — temperature °C

Source 2 Aerial map of San Joaquin valley

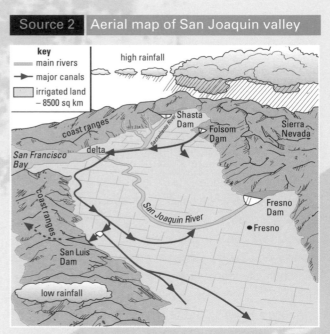

key
— main rivers
➤ major canals
□ irrigated land – 8500 sq km

high rainfall
Shasta Dam
Folsom Dam
Sierra Nevada
coast ranges
Sacramento River
delta
San Francisco Bay
coast ranges
San Joaquin River
Fresno Dam
● Fresno
San Luis Dam
low rainfall

Source 3 The Shasta Dam

Intensive market gardening
the Netherlands

Market gardening or **horticulture** involves the cultivation of fruit, vegetables and flowers on small plots of land. It is one of the most **intensive** forms of farming. Traditionally market gardens were found close to urban areas where produce could be sold as fresh as possible. Today, with improvements in transport, a market location is less important. The ideal climate for horticulture is a Mediterranean one – a mild winter and an early spring. However, these conditions can be artificially created in glasshouses. The Netherlands has become a specialist region: the coastal area of Westland is called 'the city of glass'.

The Netherlands devotes 27 per cent of its land to farming, with whole areas dedicated to producing fruit, vegetables or flowers (Source 1). There are several reasons for this.

- Almost 50 per cent of the land has been reclaimed from the sea. The new areas of land are called the Polders and have a fertile, peat and clay soil.
- Much of the land is flat, and there are plenty of waterways providing irrigation.
- Dutch farmers have access to cheap natural gas, which is used to heat the glasshouses (Source 2).
- A good transport network makes it easier to reach the local markets of Amsterdam, Rotterdam and the Hague, and more distant places.

What makes market gardening intensive? One farmer in Westland, south of the Hague, described what made his farm intensive. 'The Polder lands are very expensive, so the land has to be used almost continuously, using crop rotation, to keep the soil fertile. My farm is 2.25 hectares, which is more than twice the average size. Market gardening is labour-intensive, so we need plenty of people to work on the farms especially at harvest time. It is a costly business, and we can only sell produce which will give us a high price, if we are to make a profit.'

Source 1	Market gardening in the Netherlands

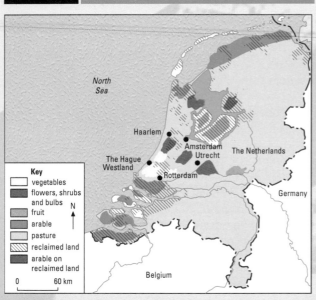

Key
- vegetables
- flowers, shrubs and bulbs
- fruit
- arable
- pasture
- reclaimed land
- arable on reclaimed land

0   60 km

Source 2	The city of glass

1 Look at the photograph on page 151 carefully and devise five questions you might ask the owner of this arable farm.

2 Copy and then complete the farming system for a market garden below. Use the words in the box below to help you.

INPUTS   PROCESSES   OUTPUTS

physical

human

Words: apples, market, pears, seeds, labour, harvesting, feed-back loop, rainfall, milking, land, fertiliser, sunshine, crop spraying, celery, pesticides, greenhouses, cucumber, fertiliser, planting.

3 Explain the difference between:
  a arable and pastoral farming
  b intensive and extensive farming
  c shifting cultivation and nomadic herding.

4 Copy and complete the following sentences:
Land not used for growing crops is called ....
A tax on imports is a ....
Excess food stored in warehouses is a food ....

5 The European Union has a Common Agricultural Policy (CAP).
  a Why was the Common Agricultural Policy formed?
  b Read the sentences in Source 1 below. Then decide whether they are problems or achievements created by the Common Agricultural Policy. Write them out in a table in the following way.

Source 1   Common Agricultural Policy

Problems	Achievements
• Food prices have risen.	• Use of machinery leads to higher yields.

• Farms are bigger and more efficient.

• Too much food leads to food mountains.

• Europe can produce much of its own food, so does not need to import as much.

• More money for farmers.

• Large fields help cause more erosion.

• Many farmers have second jobs, so they spend less time on the land.

• Some areas of Europe have got richer whilst others are poorer.

• The subsidies are expensive. 70% of the EU's budget is spent on farming.

6 Study Source 2 below, then answer the questions.

| Source 2 | Land use on a Nassau farm |

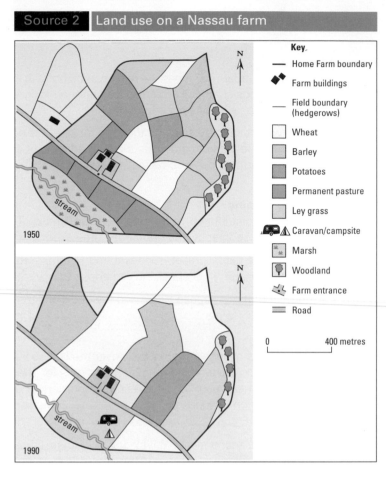

a What was the main land-use in
  i 1950 and
  ii 1990?

b State three ways in which the cultivated land was increased between 1950 and 1990.

c What has happened to the size of the fields?

d Explain fully why the field size has changed?

e Why might local environmentalists object to the change?

f Suggest other ways in which the farmer might have tried to supplement the basic income of the farm?

7 Use your local library, encyclopaedias or CD-Rom to produce a Farm File on any one or more of the following farming types:
  • plantations
  • shifting cultivation
  • rice cultivation
  • dairy farming
  • arable farming

Your File should include information on:
• the location of farming type
• the farming system – the inputs, processes and outputs of the farming type.

Where appropriate try to describe:
• changes to the farming type
• advantages and disadvantages of the farming type you have chosen.

1 Types of farming

There are many different farming types. Farming can be both an industry (commercial) and a means of survival (subsistence). Farmers in less economically developed countries, like India, are more likely to be subsistence farmers.

Farms can differ with respect to size and the amount of effort needed to run them. They can be intensive, like the market gardens in the Netherlands, or extensive, like hill farming in the Lake District. Farming can also be viewed as a system with inputs, processes and outputs.

2 Factors affecting farming

There is a distinctive distribution of farming types in Britain. The pattern of farming is influenced by physical geography and human factors.

Physical factors include rainfall, relief, sunshine hours, temperature and soil type. Human factors include the availability of capital and closeness to markets.

Britain is a member of the European Union and the decisions the EU makes can influence what is grown on British farms.

3 Agriculture in change

Farming worldwide has changed dramatically over the last 50 years. In the UK, farms are now larger, use more machinery and employ fewer people. The rural landscape has also changed. Today's farmers earn an increasing proportion of their income from non-agricultural activities such as tourism.

4 Farming and famine

Some farmers in less economically developed countries (LEDCs) struggle to produce enough food for their families to eat. At the same time, developments in science and technology are increasing yields. This means that more food can be produced, but often, as in India, the benefits are not equally distributed. Famines do still occur. They are caused by human and physical factors. They can result in a number of diseases and even in death if the famine is prolonged.

5 Farming around the world

In the UK, arable farming is found in lowland areas such as East Anglia and pastoral farming in upland areas such as the Lake District. Much of the farming in the UK is mixed.

In India rice is grown for subsistence, but quite intensively. Indian farmers often get more than one crop each year. The Fulani tribe in West Africa are pastoralists who have traditionally been nomadic. When they are encouraged to settle in one place overgrazing is a problem.

Farming change need not always involve expensive methods. Low-cost 'appropriate technology' is being used to help provide irrigation water for poor farmers in Peru.
Arid landscapes like those in California have, as a result of large-scale and costly irrigation schemes, been turned into productive agricultural areas. However, such large-scale schemes may prove costly to the environment.

World development

The Japanese and Bedouin life styles are a world apart

Measuring development

The photographs on page 171 show two scenes of life in different parts of the world today. The children in the photographs can expect very different lives. Those in the Bedouin camp are lucky to survive childhood, and will have fewer material possessions than those in Japan. The photographs illustrate the differences in 'quality of life' and development between countries.

The level of development of a country can be measured. The most common measure is the **Gross National Product** (GNP) per person. This measures the wealth of a country. Source 1 gives you some values for different countries. It is a useful measure but it does have limitations. Some countries have a high GNP per person because they are rich in oil and their

Source 1 | **Gross National Product for different countries**

Gross National Product per capita (per person) is the total value of all of the goods and services produced in a country in one year divided by the number of people. It is measured in US dollars ($) and includes the net income from overseas.

Country	GNP US $ per person	Birth rate per 1000	Death rate per 1000	Adult literacy %	Life expectancy years	Calorie intake per day	% of labour force in agriculture	Population per doctor	Infant mortality per 1000
Japan	31 450	10	7	100	79	2822	3	613	4
Sweden	24 830	13	12	100	78	3031	3	322	5
USA	24 750	15	9	96	76	3644	2	408	8
Kuwait	23 350	25	2	73	74	3127	1	739	12
UK	17 970	13	11	100	76	3259	2	623	7
Libya	6500	42	8	64	63	3393	13	862	68
Brazil	3020	25	8	82	66	2703	23	729	58
Bolivia	770	36	10	78	56	2096	40	2331	71
Bangladesh	220	36	12	35	53	1925	67	6615	108
Ethiopia	100	46	16	5	47	1715	73	41 075	120

population is very small. The wealth may be owned by just a few rich people.

In most countries, wealth is not shared equally and so the GNP figure hides great differences in wealth within countries. Source 2 shows how the world can be divided up using GNP.

Source 2 | **The world divided up using GNP**

The More Economically Developed countries (MEDCs) are those with the highest GNP. Most of these countries have a GNP of over $3000 per person, some over $7000 per person. These are the richer, more industrialised countries of the 'North'.
In contrast the Less Economically Developed Countries (LEDCs) have a GNP of less than $3000 per person. These include the poorer, less industrialised countries of the 'South'.

NORTH

Tropic of Cancer

Equator 0°

Tropic of Capricorn

SOUTH

Key

North = MEDCs

South = LEDCs

43 least economically developed countries (GNP per capita under US $100)

Indicators of development

For a long time people used GNP alone to measure the level of development of a country. Today the meaning of development has been widened. Other indicators, many of them linked to the quality of life in countries, are now used to measure development (Source 3).

Human Development Index

In 1990 the United Nation's Development Programme introduced the **Human Development Index (HDI)**. The index is calculated by giving each country a score based on the income of the population, life expectancy and a measure of education. The final score ranges from 0 for the poorest to 1 for the best. Source 4 shows that the pattern is very similar to the one for GNP. The highest scores are mostly the MEDCs. The lowest scores are mostly the LEDCs. But the index does produce some different results:

- Japan has the highest HDI (0.993)
- Guinea in West Africa is bottom with an HDI of 0.045
- countries like Sri Lanka and Tanzania rank higher than they would if only GNP were used.

Source 3 Indicators of development

Development Indicator	LEDCs	MEDCs
Jobs	High % work in farming e.g. Bangladesh 67%. Low % work in industry and services.	Low % work in farming e.g. in the UK 2%. Higher % work in industry and services.
Housing	Poor quality often with no water supply, sewage, toilets or electricity as in some shanty towns.	Higher standards, most with all the services.
Diet	Low calorie intake, average 2000 per day. Often rely on one main food e.g. rice, potatoes, which all have little protein.	High calorie intake, average 3600 per day. Variety of foods high in protein.
Health Life expectancy is the average number of years people live. Infant mortality is the number of children per 1000 who die before they are 1 year old.	High rates of infant mortality – can be over 30%. Low life expectancy, as low as 45–50 years. Shortage of doctors and hospital beds. More diseases which spread rapidly e.g. cholera, malaria.	Low rates of infant mortality and higher life expectancy – over 70 years. More doctors and hospital beds per person. Less disease.
Education Literacy is the % of adults who can read and write.	Literacy can be under 50%. Many only have primary education in makeshift schools. Little education for women.	Literacy 100% in many countries. Compulsory primary and secondary education.
Population Death rate is the number of deaths per 1000 of the population. Birth rate is the number of births per 1000 of the population.	High growth rates, large % children so pressure on resources e.g. food, schools, hospitals. High BR, falling DR	Low growth rates, lower % children. Higher % old people. Less pressure on resources. Low BRs + DRs
Trade	Rely on export of foods and raw materials i.e. primary products. Most are low in value and prices fluctuate. Import costly manufactured goods. Often a trade deficit.	Buy cheaper raw materials from LEDCs. High % of manufacturing, sold at higher prices to rest of the world.

Source 4 The world divided up using HDI

Human development index (HDI) value 1993

- 0.8 – 1
- 0.6 – 0.79
- 0.4 – 0.59
- 0.2 – 0.39

No data available

Trade and interdependence

Trade is the flow of goods and services between people. There are many different types of trade as Source 1 shows. International trade involves selling goods to other countries (**exports**) and buying goods from other countries (**imports**). Trade is essential and Source 2 shows why countries need to trade.

Why do we trade?

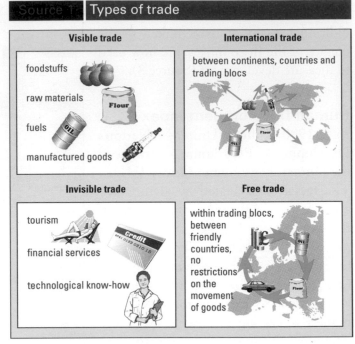

Source 1 | Types of trade

The balance of trade

The **balance of trade** is the difference between the costs of imports and the value of exports. Some countries earn vast profits from their exports and need to import very little. These countries have a trade surplus. They become richer and more developed. Other countries earn much less from their exports, and imports cost much more. These countries have a trade deficit and they become poorer.

The world pattern of trade

The pattern of trade is different for the MEDCs and the LEDCs (Source 3). Most trade is between the richer countries such as Japan, USA and the members of the European Union (EU). The MEDCs have a greater volume of trade and their goods are higher in value. The LEDCs have little to export and their products are relatively low in value as they are usually raw materials or commodities, to which little value has yet been added. Many LEDCs rely on just one or two export products.

Source 3 | The world pattern of Trade

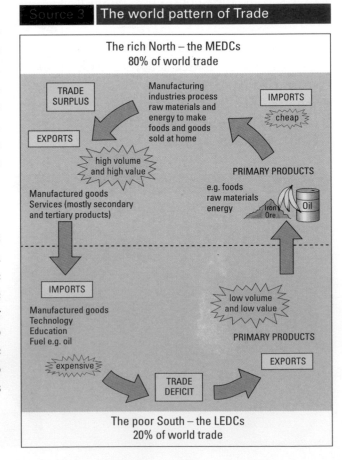

Trade groupings

Some countries have grouped together to form **trading blocs** (Source 4). The European Union is one example. Trading blocs allow member countries to buy and sell goods often with no tariffs (taxes) being charged, so goods traded inside the bloc are cheaper. The countries can sometimes negotiate lower prices for imported goods because the countries act together. The richer countries of the North can often dictate the price they will pay for goods from the LEDCs.

Source 4	Some trading blocs

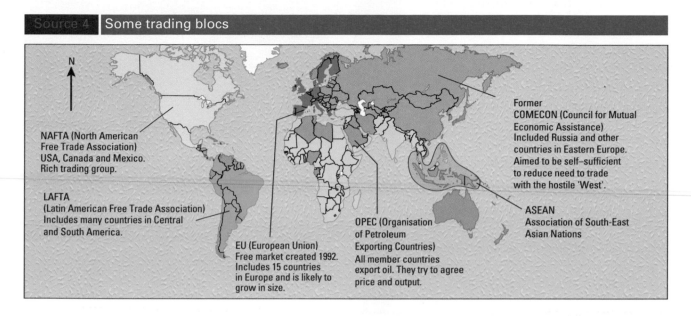

NAFTA (North American Free Trade Association) USA, Canada and Mexico. Rich trading group.

LAFTA (Latin American Free Trade Association) Includes many countries in Central and South America.

EU (European Union) Free market created 1992. Includes 15 countries in Europe and is likely to grow in size.

OPEC (Organisation of Petroleum Exporting Countries) All member countries export oil. They try to agree price and output.

Former COMECON (Council for Mutual Economic Assistance) Included Russia and other countries in Eastern Europe. Aimed to be self–sufficient to reduce need to trade with the hostile 'West'.

ASEAN Association of South-East Asian Nations

Dependence or interdependence?

The MEDCs rely upon foods, fuels and minerals from the LEDCs. The LEDCs rely on the money from exports to buy machinery and technology from the MEDCs. This helps the LEDCs along the path of development. A two-way process would be fair, but trade is *not* fair:

- The primary products mostly produced by LEDCs are low in value.
- Prices of primary products fluctuate, and are often controlled by the MEDCs.
- The value of primary products has not risen at the same rate as the value of manufactured goods.
- Tariff barriers act against the LEDCs.

As a result, a huge trade gap has opened up. Many LEDCs have huge **trade deficits**. They have needed to borrow money from the banks of the North and have huge debts. Many cannot afford to repay the interest, let alone the loan. The LEDCs have little control over the trade (Source 5).

Source 5	The trade trap

Many of the poorer countries in the world are in debt. Many also suffer from natural disasters such as floods, drought, famine and tropical storms. The MEDCs can help in two main ways:

1 By fair and free trade The MEDCs could lower the tariffs on goods processed in the LEDCs and pay more for the primary products which they buy. Fair trade and tariffs are discussed by the countries of the world at the **GATT** talks but, as Source 1 shows, progress is difficult.

2 By giving aid It has been suggested that 0.7 per cent of the GNP of every MEDC should be given as **aid,** rising to 1 per cent in the year 2000. This target is rarely reached, as Source 2 shows.

Aid

Aid is the transfer of money, goods and expertise to assist the development of the world's poorest countries (Source 3).

Source 1	General Agreement on Tariffs and Trade (GATT)

Source 2	The world's best donors of aid, 1990

Donor country	Aid in billions of dollars	% of GNP
Netherlands	2.6	0.94*
France	9.4	0.79*
Canada	2.5	0.44
Germany	6.3	0.42
Italy	3.4	0.32
Japan	9.1	0.31
UK	2.6	0.28
USA	17.4	0.21
Others	7.1	0.51

*above the recommended level of 0.7% GNP

Source 3	Types of aid

Official Development Aid (ODA)

This includes bilateral grants, loans and technical assistance. This is the aid which goes from government to government. The LEDC designs the development scheme.

Voluntary aid

This is given by individuals rather than governments to national and international charities, for example Oxfam, Red Cross.

Multilateral aid

A country provides aid through a third party such as the United Nations, the World Bank or the IMF (International Monetary Fund). This is a growing source of aid and is not tied to any one country.

Emergency short-term aid

This is aid in the form of food, shelter, medical supplies and water that is sent to countries following a natural disaster.

Aid can come from two main sources:

1 Governments Governments are involved in two types of aid. The first is **bilateral aid** where the government of the country gives the aid directly to the government of the receiving country. The aid may include grants, loans and technical assistance.

The second is **multilateral aid** where a government donates aid to large international institutions like the World Bank or United Nations. These institutions then send the aid to the countries in need.

2 Non-governmental organisations (NGOs) NGOs are charitable organisations like Oxfam, the Red Cross and Save the Children. They rely on donations and fund raising events to pay for projects in poorer countries. It is sometimes called **voluntary aid** because the money is given by individuals. Projects tend to be on a smaller scale but have more of a direct effect on the lives of the local people in the LEDCs.

As well as long-term development projects, short-term **emergency aid** (food, shelter, medical supplies etc.) is given following a natural disaster. Ethiopia received emergency aid during the famines of the 1980s and 1990s.

Benefits of aid

- Long-term aid projects help a country to develop and become independent. These types of projects include schemes:
  - to improve education and skills
  - to increase crop yields to feed the local population rather than for export
  - to set up small-scale industries
  - to improve water supply and health.
- After a natural disaster short-term emergency aid such as food, clothing, shelter and medical care is a great help (Source 4).

Problems of aid

- Aid does not always match the needs of countries. India seems to receive less aid than other countries, yet there are more poor people.
- Some countries give aid with strings attached.

The donor countries look for something in return for their aid, perhaps a military base or a trade agreement. For example, the USA gave Peru large loans to explore for oil. In return Peru bought jet aircraft from the USA and allowed USA fishing boats into its waters.

- The aid often does not reach the poorest people in the rural areas. Corrupt governments may spend the aid in the urban areas and on tourism. The rich get richer and the poor get poorer.
- The LEDCs rely on aid but it is a loan to be paid back. It puts the country more in debt.
- The MEDCs have had a series of recessions, as a result of which they have given less for aid projects.

Source 4 | Where does the aid go?

Country	Number of poor (millions)	Official aid per person (US$)
India	480	1.8
China	120	1.8
Bangladesh	99	18.0
Indonesia	70	9.3
Pakistan	37	8.8

Countries with different levels of development
Brazil and Italy

Can you name any wealthy and poor areas within your local area? Differences in development can be seen within a single city, between regions in a country and between countries. Here we compare Brazil and Italy (Sources 1 and 2). A variety of indicators are used to measure the level of development:

- economic indicators, for example GNP, trade and aid
- social indicators, for example health care and education.

Source 1 | **Brazil**

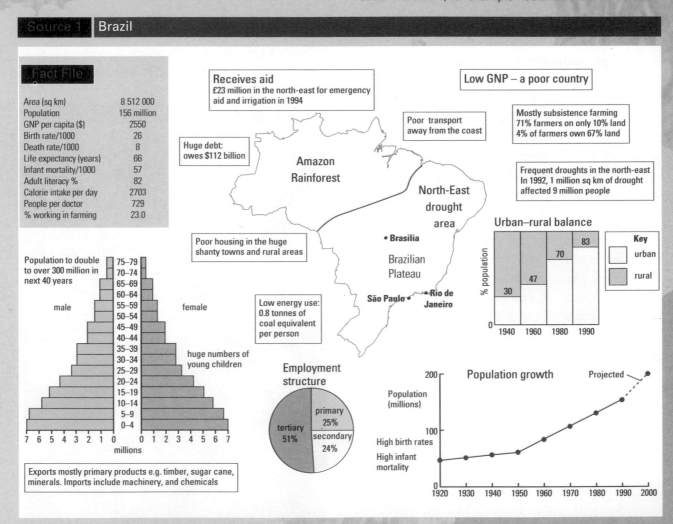

Fact File

Area (sq km)	8 512 000
Population	156 million
GNP per capita ($)	2550
Birth rate/1000	26
Death rate/1000	8
Life expectancy (years)	66
Infant mortality/1000	57
Adult literacy %	82
Calorie intake per day	2703
People per doctor	729
% working in farming	23.0

Receives aid
£23 million in the north-east for emergency aid and irrigation in 1994

Low GNP – a poor country

Poor transport away from the coast

Mostly subsistence farming 71% farmers on only 10% land 4% of farmers own 67% land

Huge debt: owes $112 billion

Amazon Rainforest

Frequent droughts in the north-east In 1992, 1 million sq km of drought affected 9 million people

North-East drought area

• Brasilia

Brazilian Plateau

São Paulo • • Rio de Janeiro

Poor housing in the huge shanty towns and rural areas

Low energy use: 0.8 tonnes of coal equivalent per person

Urban–rural balance

Key: urban, rural

Population to double to over 300 million in next 40 years

huge numbers of young children

Exports mostly primary products e.g. timber, sugar cane, minerals. Imports include machinery, and chemicals

Employment structure

tertiary 51%, primary 25%, secondary 24%

Population growth

Projected

Population (millions)

High birth rates
High infant mortality

Brazil: summary

Brazil is one of the world's less economically developed countries (LEDCs). The figures for birth rate, energy consumption and infant mortality support this. Brazil also has some characteristics expected of the MEDCs. These include the low death rate, the percentage of people living in urban areas and a trade surplus.

Since the 1960s, there has been an economic miracle in Brazil. Large-scale industries have developed, raw materials and energy resources have been exploited and the GNP has risen. But much of the country remains poor and undeveloped, especially the north-east where there are frequent droughts. The government also borrowed heavily to pay for these developments.

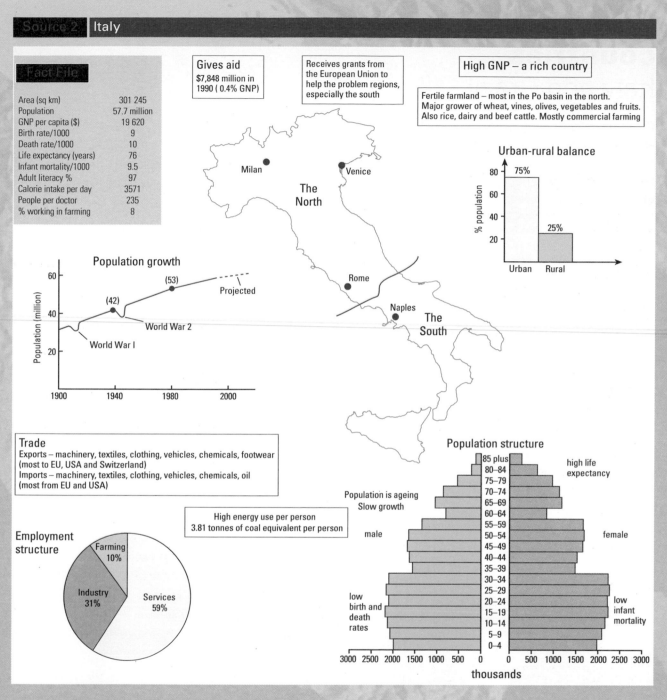

Source 2 | Italy

Fact File

Area (sq km)	301 245
Population	57.7 million
GNP per capita ($)	19 620
Birth rate/1000	9
Death rate/1000	10
Life expectancy (years)	76
Infant mortality/1000	9.5
Adult literacy %	97
Calorie intake per day	3571
People per doctor	235
% working in farming	8

Gives aid
$7,848 million in 1990 (0.4% GNP)

Receives grants from the European Union to help the problem regions, especially the south

High GNP – a rich country

Fertile farmland – most in the Po basin in the north. Major grower of wheat, vines, olives, vegetables and fruits. Also rice, dairy and beef cattle. Mostly commercial farming

Milan · Venice · The North · Rome · Naples · The South

Urban-rural balance

75% Urban · 25% Rural

Population growth

(42) (53) Projected · World War 2 · World War I

1900 1940 1980 2000

Trade
Exports – machinery, textiles, clothing, vehicles, chemicals, footwear (most to EU, USA and Switzerland)
Imports – machinery, textiles, clothing, vehicles, chemicals, oil (most from EU and USA)

High energy use per person
3.81 tonnes of coal equivalent per person

Employment structure
Farming 10%
Industry 31%
Services 59%

Population structure

85 plus, 80–84, 75–79, 70–74, 65–69, 60–64, 55–59, 50–54, 45–49, 40–44, 35–39, 30–34, 25–29, 20–24, 15–19, 10–14, 5–9, 0–4

high life expectancy
Population is ageing / Slow growth
male · female
low birth and death rates
low infant mortality

3000 2500 2000 1500 1000 500 0 500 1000 1500 2000 2500 3000
thousands

Italy: summary

Italy is one of the world's more economically developed countries (MEDCs). It has none of the characteristics of an LEDC except a small trade deficit. Italy has generally high living standards, low population growth and a high GNP. Poorer Italians are supported by welfare payments.

The country has a variety of landscapes and climates. There are large areas of fertile farmland which are used intensively to grow arable crops, vines and vegetables. The country can afford to import oil and has supplies of gas, oil and HEP (hydro-electric power). There is a long history of manufacturing and there are many different industries.

Italy also has problems. There are summer droughts and several volcanoes in the south, and there may be avalanches and the occasional earthquake in the Alps. The world recession has caused a trade deficit in recent years. Congestion and pollution are growing problems in large cities such as Milan, Venice and Rome. Perhaps Italy's greatest problems lie in the south of the country which remains quite undeveloped in many areas.

Contrasts in development within countries
Italy and Brazil

Wealth is not shared evenly within a single country. It is often concentrated in just one favoured region called the **core,** leaving other regions quite poor in comparison. These poorer regions are called the **periphery.**

Italy

Italy is a country with a north–south divide (Source 1). The north, especially the Po basin, is the core region and is wealthier and more developed than the south. The south of Italy, called the *Mezzogiorno*, is the periphery.

| Source 1 | Italy's North–South divide |

Advantages of the north:

- supplies of natural gas in the Po basin and HEP from the Alps
- more jobs in industry and services
- fertile lowland with irrigation water available
- large cities, for example Milan, Turin and Genoa connected by an efficient transport system
- close to large European markets
- better-quality housing and services and higher standard of living

Disadvantages of the south:

- mountainous relief makes communications difficult
- the climate is hot and dry in summer with a few months' drought
- heavy winter rainfall causes soil erosion and flooding
- the rocks are mostly limestone and form thin soils
- low yields of wheat, olives and vines
- poor-quality grazing for sheep and goats
- poor transport, little industry, emigration

Since 1950 the Italian government has invested money to try to improve the south. In recent years the EU has also provided grants and loans. Some new *autostradi* (motorways) have been built. New irrigation schemes allow tomatoes, citrus fruits and vegetables to be grown and some large-scale industry, such as iron and steel, and car manufacture, has located here. However, the north–south divide remains and the gap is widening.

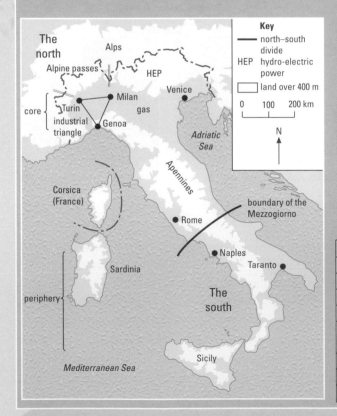

Key

— north–south divide

HEP hydro-electric power

land over 400 m

0   100   200 km

N

The north — Alps — Alpine passes — HEP — Venice — Milan — gas — core — Turin industrial triangle — Genoa — Adriatic Sea — Apennines — Corsica (France) — boundary of the Mezzogiorno — Rome — Naples — Taranto — Sardinia — periphery — The south — Mediterranean Sea — Sicily

	North Italy	South Italy
Area %	60	40
Population %	63	37
Birth rate per 1000	11	17
Death rate per 1000	10	8
Income per person (million lira)	>2500	<1600
% farm production	65	35
% share of hospital beds	74	26
% unemployment	8%	22%

Brazil

Brazil's core region is the south east of the country. The north and north east form the periphery (Source 2).

Source 2 | Brazil's south-east–north-east divide

The north east

The north east forms part of the periphery in Brazil. It is poorly developed and has many problems.

- The region suffers frequent droughts. In 1992 the drought affected 9 million people.
- Most farmers are subsistence farmers.
- The land is poor with infertile and eroded soils.
- Crop yields are low but the birth rate is high – there is not enough food to feed the population.
- The best land is used for plantations, often owned by **transnationals**. The crops are for export.
- The region has poor housing and services.
- Thousands of people have migrated from the area.

The south east

Early growth was linked to coffee-growing near São Paulo. Coffee, gold and diamonds were exported. Later, rapid growth began with the mining of iron ore, the making of steel and the manufacture of cars and ships. Services were provided for the growing number of **migrants** from the rural areas.

Why is the south east the core region?

- It is the centre of commerce, industry, education, transport and culture.
- The region has the highest standard of living in Brazil and contributes most to GNP.

However, many people live in shanty towns and there is congestion and pollution in the cities.

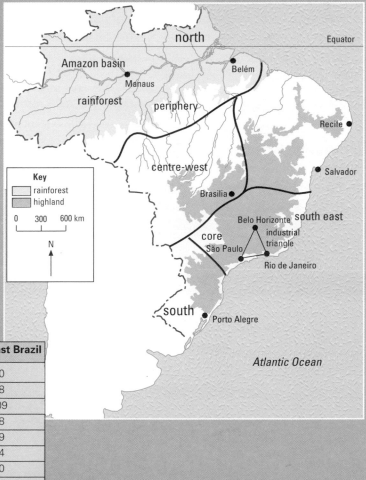

	South-east Brazil	North-east Brazil
Population %	42	30
Birth rate per 1000	22	48
Infant mortality per 1000	49	109
Life expectancy per 1000	63	48
Adult literacy%	72	39
% share of national wealth	64	14
% employed in industry	70	10
% with clean water	64	23

A trading nation
Japan

Before 1945 Japan was very isolated from the rest of the world. Few foreigners were allowed entry and there was little trade. Since 1945 there has been an economic miracle. The GNP has risen greatly and in 1989 Japan replaced the USA as the world's richest nation. Despite having very few natural resources, trade and industry have developed for the following reasons:

- Japan has no oil or iron ore, very little coal or other raw materials, and needs to import these items.
- Japan has to export to pay for the imports. Steel, chemicals, cars and ships were sold abroad (Source 1). Since the 1970s these industries have declined. They have been replaced by a growth in the electronics industry and in services.
- The Japanese have developed and manufactured many new products, for example: computers, video recorders, compact disc players and video cameras. Source 2 shows the main imports and exports of Japan today.

The reasons for Japan's economic miracle are as follows.

Economic
- modern machines and methods of working
- profits used in research to develop new products
- large home market which has become richer

Cultural
- well-educated workforce
- the workforce operate well in teams and are prepared to work long hours
- they have a high degree of loyalty to their company

Political
- strong government support for industry
- political stability

Source 1 Japan's exports

Japan has been so successful that every year there is a huge trade surplus. It was $ 135 billion in 1995. The country is very dependent upon the rest of the world to supply the raw materials that its industry needs, and to provide the market for the goods it makes. Japan is **interdependent** with many countries.

Japan's success has also brought some problems. Japan has been in trouble in the world over its trading policies. Japan has the benefit of free trade in many areas of the world yet charges high tariffs on goods entering Japan.

Source 2 Main imports and exports of Japan

Imports		Exports
fuel and energy (20.4%)		motor vehicles (17.6%)
food and drink (15.1%)		office machinery (7.0%)
raw materials (13.3%)	Tokyo / Osaka	iron and steel (5.4%)
machinery and vehicles (12.6%)	0 500 km	chemicals (5.4%)

Dominica is one of the Windward Islands in the Caribbean (Source 1). Today, the islands are mostly dependent upon a single crop – bananas. This is called **primary product dependency.**

The banana industry employs over 15 000 people out of a population of 88 000. The family-run farms are small – about 5 acres. Vegetables to feed the family are grown on 1 acre and 4 acres grow bananas. The bananas have to be perfect or they will not sell in Europe.

Dominica is a poor country, its GNP is only $2570 per person. Growing bananas is not a very profitable activity and 50 per cent of the turnover goes on fertilisers, pesticides, blue plastic sheets to protect the crop from insects and the cardboard boxes used to pack the bananas (Source 2).

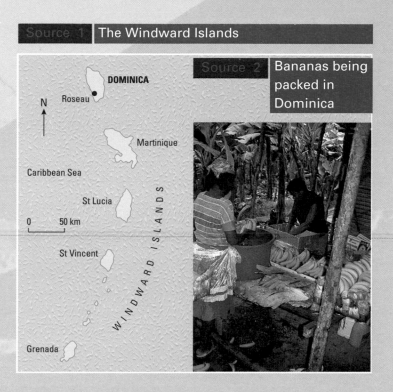

Source 1 The Windward Islands

DOMINICA
Roseau
N
Martinique
Caribbean Sea
St Lucia
0   50 km
St Vincent
WINDWARD ISLANDS
Grenada

Source 2 Bananas being packed in Dominica

Source 3 Problems in Dominica

Tragedy for Dominica if Geest pulls out

Geest (established banana traders since colonial times) are threatening to pull out of the banana industry in Dominica. Two out of every three bananas produced are eaten in the UK. Talks to negotiate a new contract with Geest and the EU are taking place.

Hurricane David destroys banana crop

Dominica on a loser

Recent reports show that only 25 per cent of the money earned from bananas ends up in Dominica.

Dominica is dependent on bananas because of:

- the British influence in colonial times: each person in the UK still eats an average of 8.2 kilos of bananas a year
- the climate and relief are suitable for bananas but little else grows well
- there are few raw materials or energy supplies to develop other industries
- there are few natural attractions to bring in many tourists, whereas other Caribbean Islands have developed because of tourism.

Look at Source 3 to discover some of the problems facing the banana growers.

SPAT, the Small Projects Assistance Team in Dominica, is working to:

- rebuild plantations after the hurricanes
- develop livestock farming, e.g. pigs
- diversify crops, e.g. root crops, herbal medicines
- negotiate new contracts with the EU.

Dominica needs to reduce its dependency on bananas in order to develop in the future.

Assisting development
British overseas aid and Bangladesh

Britain is one of the wealthy countries of the world and a major aid donor. Britain gives over £1500 million a year, but it is still not up to the O.7 per cent of GNP expected by the United Nations. Britain gives aid to help poorer countries to:

- raise their standard of living
- make better use of land and resources
- preserve the environment
- improve health and education
- cope with natural disasters.

Britain's official aid programme is managed by the Overseas Development Administration (ODA). The ODA is part of the Foreign and Commonwealth Office. Over 50 per cent of Britain's aid is spent on bilateral aid, which is paid directly to the governments of individual countries.

Source 1 | British aid and Bangladesh

Problems of Bangladesh	The Five Year Development Plan	Aims of British aid
• lack of natural resources, e.g. minerals, energy	• reduce population growth	• to reach the poorest people
• high dependence on agriculture	• expand employment	• to give priority to women's development
• floods and hurricanes	• primary education for all	• to involve British goods and services
• low literacy rates	• improved technology	• to focus on agriculture, energy, transport, health, family planning and education
• poor communications	• self-sufficiency in food	
• a huge population and high population growth	• greater economic growth	
	• improve standards of living and health care	

Partners in development: Britain and Bangladesh

Britain has a special relationship with Bangladesh. The country has received over £700 million in aid since 1971 when Bangladesh gained independence. Britain gives Bangladesh different types of aid.

- **Bilateral aid,** since 1974, has been in the form of grants. This money does not have to be repaid and there are no interest charges.
- **Multilateral aid,** is given through contributions to the World Bank, the European Union, the Asian Development Bank and the World Food Programme.
- **Non-governmental organisations,** include Oxfam, CARE, Christian Aid, Save the Children and the British Red Cross. They work at the grass-roots level in communities (Source 2).

  Britain works with Bangladesh to support the Five Year Development Plan which aims to tackle the country's most serious problems (Source1). Source 3 shows more about British aid in Bangladesh.

Source 2 | Health care

Source 3 Aid to Bangladesh

Agriculture

The Deep Tubewell Project aims to increase food production. It will allow the farmers to grow rice in the dry season. Britain has given £17 million towards building 4000 wells. The wells will irrigate 130 000 hectares of land. The money provides consultants as well as diesel engines, electric pumps, well casings and computer equipment. Other agricultural schemes include:

• deep water rice research project to increase yields, develop new varieties, and improve methods of pest control
• tea project to improve quality and output
• improving cattle health
• developing fish hatcheries.

Power and energy

Greater Dhaka, the region around the capital of Bangladesh, has a population of over 20 million. It uses one-third of the country's power and demand is rising. Britain began giving aid for a power project in the region in 1974. Since then £63 million has been spent on over 2500 km of transmission cables and 14 new substations.

Britain has also given aid for a gas fired power station at Ashuganj in Bangladesh and for the development of gas fields. This will reduce the need for Bangladesh to import fuels.

Emergency aid

The British government often sends emergency aid for refugees and disaster relief. In the last decade Britain has given large amounts of food aid to Bangladesh. In several years the crops have failed because of natural disasters. The aid is provided as wheat and it often totals over 100 000 tonnes in a year.

Non-governmental organisations

Other work in Bangladesh is done by NGOs (or charities) such as Oxfam, the Red Cross and Save The Children. The National Lottery now provides some funding and the British government also supports NGOs. The amount of government funding has increased in recent years because of the huge floods in the 1980s and 1990s.

In 1985 Christian Aid established the Nari Kendra, a women's centre near Dhaka. It trains women in health care, literacy, numeracy and other skills. The ODA gave £55 000 to support the project.

Multilateral aid

About 40 per cent of the British government's aid is paid to large international agencies such as the World Bank, the European Union and the United Nations. Bangladesh has received over $520 million of multilateral aid. The money is used in a range of projects to improve agriculture, power and social conditions.

1 Study the photographs on page 171. Write down five differences in the quality of life that the photographs suggest.

2 **a** What does GNP stand for? What does it measure?
  b Use the GNP data in Source 1 on page 172 for this exercise.
    List those countries with a GNP per capita (**i**) above $20 000 and (**ii**) below $10 000.
  c Using the two lists from **b** say which list is made up of MEDCs and which is made up of LEDCs.
  d Give two reasons why GNP is not always a good indicator of development.

3 Name six indicators, other than GNP, which can be used to show the level of development for a country.

4 Scattergraphs can show whether there is a link between GNP and the other indicators of development. Draw scattergraphs between GNP and some of the other indicators shown on Source 1 on page 172. Source 1 below shows the example of GNP and birth rate. Write a sentence below each of your graphs to say what it shows.

Source 1	Drawing scattergraphs

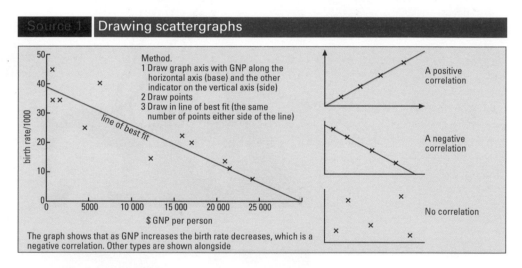

Method.
1 Draw graph axis with GNP along the horizontal axis (base) and the other indicator on the vertical axis (side)
2 Draw points
3 Draw in line of best fit (the same number of points either side of the line)

A positive correlation

A negative correlation

No correlation

The graph shows that as GNP increases the birth rate decreases, which is a negative correlation. Other types are shown alongside

5 **a** Define the following terms: trade; international trade; exports; imports; balance of trade; trade deficit; trade surplus.
  b Give three reasons why countries need to trade.

6 Study Source 5 on page 175. Write an account of what the cartoon strip is trying to show about the trade trap.

7 **a** What is aid and why do the LEDCs need it?
  b According to the UN, how much aid should each MEDC give?

8 **a** Name the four types of aid and write a sentence to say what each one means.
  b Draw up a table like the one below to show some of the benefits and problems of aid.

Benefits of aid	Problems of aid

9 a Produce a table in summary form to show the differences between Brazil and Italy.
b In what ways is Brazil as developed as Italy?
c In what ways is Italy like a less economically developed country?
d What problems do Brazil and Italy share?

10 Italy and Brazil both have differences in development within their countries. You could use these questions for one or both countries.
a What do you understand by the core and periphery in a country?
b Draw a sketch map and label some of the main features of the country.
c On your sketch map clearly mark the core and periphery.
d Quote three statistics that show the differences between the two regions.
e List five advantages of the core and five disadvantages of the periphery.

11 a Find out some of the indicators of development for Dominica. Is the country an MEDC or an LEDC? Explain your answer.
b Give four reasons why Dominica is dependent on the banana trade.
c What are the problems caused by having only one main source of income?
d How can Dominica solve its problems?

12 Choose two of the ways Britain helps Bangladesh by giving aid. Name the type of aid being given and describe the work that was done.

13 Study the cartoon in Source 2. What does the cartoon tell you about trade and aid between the MEDCs and the LEDCs?

| Source 2 | North and South |

'Do you realise I have you under my control?'

187

1 Measuring development

The most common measurement of development is by Gross National Product (GNP) which measures the wealth of a country. However, other measures are often used such as employment, housing, diet, health care and education.

Indicators of development have been used to divide countries into two broad groups – the more economically developed countries (MEDCs) and the less economically developed countries (LEDCs). The MEDCs are the richer, industrialised countries, such as Japan, the UK and the USA, mostly in the northern hemisphere. The LEDCs are the poorer countries, for example Ethiopia, Bangladesh and Brazil, mostly located in the southern hemisphere.

2 Trade and interdependence

Trade is the flow of goods and services between people. Countries which need to import goods also need to export in order to pay for the imports. The balance between exports and imports is called the balance of trade. It may be a deficit or a surplus. In general the MEDCs have a trade surplus while the LEDCs have a trade deficit. Many countries have formed trading blocs with neighbouring countries. One example is the European Union (EU).

3 Fair trade and aid

At the moment trade is not always fair. The MEDCs apply tariffs to imported goods which stop the LEDCs earning more for their manufactures. The GATT talks tend to be ruled by the powerful MEDCs so little change has occurred in trade.

The UN has suggested that all the MEDCs give 0.7 per cent of their GNP in aid to poorer countries but this rarely happens.

There are several different types of aid: bilateral or government to government; multilateral, for example the World Bank and United Nations; non-governmental, which involves the charities, and emergency aid following a natural disaster.

4 Contrasts in development: Brazil and Italy

Countries have different levels of development, for example Italy is classified as an MEDC while Brazil is an LEDC. The level of development is measured by a range of indicators. Some are economic, such as GNP, employment, aid, while others are social, such as population, health and education.

There may also be different levels of development within a country. A core – the wealthy growth area – and a periphery – the less developed area – can be recognised. In Italy, for example, the core is in the north of the country while the south forms the periphery.

5 A trading nation: Japan

A country like Japan with few natural resources has had to import raw materials for industry. To pay for the imports the country must export the manufactured goods. Japan has been so successful that it is now a major trading nation.

Energy

An oil rig in the North Sea

World energy resources

Energy is one of the most important of all the world's resources. We need energy to keep us warm and to cook with. It gives us light and drives machinery for transport and industry. Fortunately our natural environment provides us with a wide range of energy sources. **Fossil fuels** such as coal, oil, gas and fuelwood; uranium; the sun, water and wind can all be used to produce energy. Source 1 shows the relative importance of each of these today.

Energy sources such as fossil fuels are classed as **non-renewable** – once used up they cannot be replaced. Newer energy sources are often **renewable** e.g. solar and wind power – they can be used again and again. These are often **sustainable,** and are likely to play an increasingly more important role in the future.

| Source 1 | World energy production |

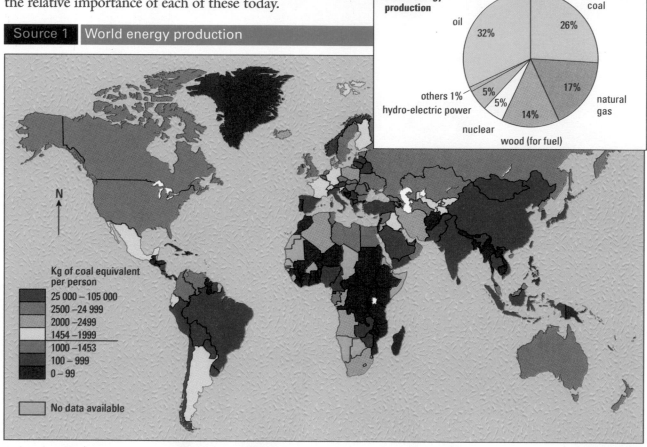

World energy production

- coal 26%
- oil 32%
- natural gas 17%
- wood (for fuel) 14%
- nuclear 5%
- hydro-electric power 5%
- others 1%

Kg of coal equivalent per person
- 25 000 – 105 000
- 2500 – 24 999
- 2000 – 2499
- 1454 – 1999
- 1000 – 1453
- 100 – 999
- 0 – 99

No data available

Who supplies the world's energy?

Seventy-five per cent of the world's energy comes from fossil fuels. Source 1 also shows that these are not very evenly distributed across the world. The USA, Canada, former USSR, Western Europe, Australia, China and the Middle East contain most of the world's coal, oil and natural gas. Western Europe and North America were the first regions to become industrialised. Their early industrial development was helped by the abundance of fossil fuels, particularly coal. Many of the world's MEDCs (more economically developed countries) are found here today.

Source 1 does not take into account the use of wood and **biomass** fuels (fuels made from burning or rotting plants and vegetation. Many people in LEDCs (less economically developed countries) rely on these to supply their energy needs.

Who uses the world's energy?

Europe and North America use 70 per cent of the world's energy (Source 2), although only 20 per cent of the world's population live there. These regions developed their industries quickly using fossil fuels. Today, with many of their own reserves falling or exhausted, they need to import energy to meet demands, especially oil.

| Source 2 | World energy consumption |

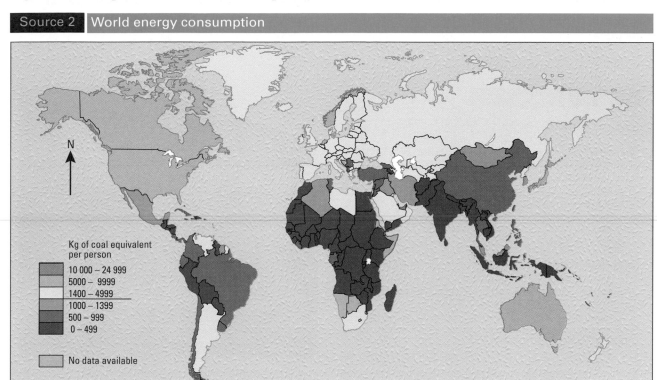

Kg of coal equivalent per person

- 10 000 – 24 999
- 5000 – 9999
- 1400 – 4999
- 1000 – 1399
- 500 – 999
- 0 – 499

No data available

| Source 3 | Energy in the city |

A comparison of Sources 1 and 2 shows quite clearly that the world's major producers of energy are also the major consumers. The amount of energy a country uses is a good indicator of its stage of development (Source 3). The presence of energy resources has obviously been a major factor in the industrial development of some countries. Most of today's MEDCs have substantial fossil fuel deposits – either currently or in the past. The main exception is Japan, whose industry has developed despite a lack of energy resources. Even so, Japan is looking to nuclear power in the future, rather than continuing to rely on importing oil.

As fossil fuels start to run out and countries become more aware of the environmental problems caused by their use, the relative importance of different types of energy seems likely to change.

Non-renewable energy

The world's energy resources can be divided into non-renewable and renewable resources. Non-renewable resources are finite – once they are used up they cannot be replaced because they take too long to form or regrow. They include the major fossil fuels formed over tens of thousands of years – coal, oil and natural gas, plus uranium (used in nuclear power stations) and fuel wood.

Fact File Coal

Status non-renewable fossil fuel

Description formed underground from decaying plant matter

Lifespan 250–300 years

% share of world energy consumption 26

Main producers USA, Western Europe, former USSR, China, Australia, India, South Africa

Energy uses electricity, heating, coke

✓ **advantages** high world reserves; newer mines are highly mechanised

✗ **disadvantages** pollution – CO_2, the major greenhouse gas responsible for global warming; SO_2 the main gas responsible for acid rain; mining can be difficult and dangerous, opencast pits destroy land; heavy/bulky to transport

Fact File Oil

Status non-renewable fossil fuel

Description formed underground from decaying animal/plant matter

Lifespan 50 years

% share of world energy consumption 32

Main producers Middle East, USA, former USSR, Mexico, China, UK, Norway, Canada, Venezuela

Energy uses electricity, petroleum, diesel, fuel oils, liquid petroleum gas, coke and many non-energy uses, e.g. plastics, medicines, fertilisers

✓ **advantages** variety of uses; fairly easy to transport; efficient; less pollution than coal

✗ **disadvantages** low reserves; some air pollution; danger of spills (especially at sea) and explosions

Fact File Natural gas

Status   non-renewable fossil fuel

Description   formed underground from decaying animal/plant matter; often found with oil

Lifespan   70 years

% share of world energy consumption   17

Main producers   USA, Canada, former USSR, Mexico, Venezuela, China, Algeria

Energy uses   electricity, cooking, heating

✓ **advantages**   efficient; clean – least polluting of the fossil fuels; easy to transport

X **disadvantages**   explosions; some air pollution

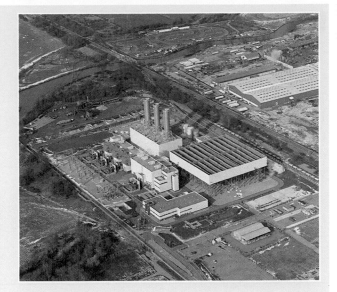

Fact File Fuelwood

Status   non-renewable fossil fuel

Description   trees, usually in natural environment, not grown specifically for fuel

Lifespan   variable within each country, but declining

% share of world energy consumption   14

Main producers of energy   LEDCs, especially in Africa and Asia

Energy uses   heating, cooking (also used for building homes and fences)

✓ **advantages**   easily available, collected daily by local people; free; replanting possible

X **disadvantages**   trees quickly used; time-consuming – wood collected daily; deforestation leading to other problems (soil erosion, desertification); replanting cannot keep pace with consumption

Fact File Nuclear

Status   non-renewable

Description   heavy metal (uranium) element found naturally in rock deposits

Lifespan   unknown

% share of world energy consumption   5

Main producers   Canada, USA, Spain, former USSR, Australia, Namibia, South Africa

Energy uses   used in a chain reaction to produce heat for electricity

✓ **advantages**   clean; fewer greenhouse gases; efficient; uses very small amounts of raw materials; small amounts of waste

X **disadvantages**   dangers of radiation; high cost of building and decommissioning power stations; problems over disposal of waste; accident at Chernobyl raised public fears; Sellafield (Cumbria) has had a number of minor leaks

Renewable energy

Fossil fuels are non-renewable energy sources. However, there are many sources which can be classed as renewable sources. These include the use of water – hydro-electric power, tidal and wave; the wind; the sun; geothermal and biomass/biogas.

Renewable resources are generally cleaner than non-renewable sources, but as yet produce only 6 per cent of the world's energy needs. Solar, tidal, wave, geothermal and biomass/biogas are often called 'alternative' energies.

Fact File | Hydro-electric power

Status renewable

Description good, regular supply of water needed; water held in a reservoir, channelled through pipes to a turbine

% share of world energy consumption 5

Main producers Canada, USA , former USSR, Brazil, China

Energy uses electricity

✓ **advantages** very clean; reservoirs/dams can also control flooding/provide water in times of shortage; often in remote, mountainous, sparsely populated areas

✗ **disadvantages** large areas of land flooded; silt trapped behind dam; lake silts up; visual pollution from pylons

Fact File | Tidal

Status renewable

Description tidal water drives turbines

% share of world energy consumption less than 1

Main producers France, former USSR, China, Canada

Energy uses electricity

✓ **advantages** large schemes could produce a lot of electricity; clean; barrage can protect coasts from erosion

✗ **disadvantages** very expensive to build; few suitable sites; disrupts coastal ecosystems and shipping

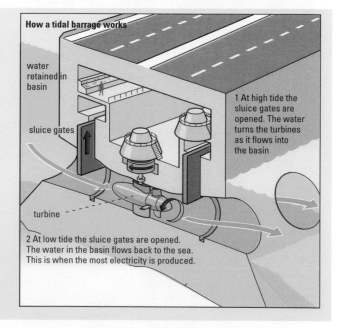

How a tidal barrage works

water retained in basin

sluice gates

turbine

1 At high tide the sluice gates are opened. The water turns the turbines as it flows into the basin

2 At low tide the sluice gates are opened. The water in the basin flows back to the sea. This is when the most electricity is produced.

Fact File — Solar

Status renewable

Description solar panels or photovoltaic cells using sunlight

% share of world energy consumption less than 1

Main producers USA, India

Energy uses direct heating, electricity

✓ **advantages** could be used in most parts of the world – unlimited supplies; clean; can be built in to new buildings; efficient

X **disadvantages** expensive: needs sunlight – cloud/night = no energy; unlikely to produce large amounts of energy

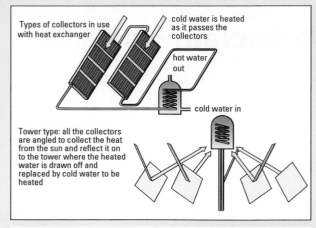

Types of collectors in use with heat exchanger

cold water is heated as it passes the collectors

hot water out

cold water in

Tower type: all the collectors are angled to collect the heat from the sun and reflect it on to the tower where the heated water is drawn off and replaced by cold water to be heated

Fact File — Wind

Status renewable

Description wind drives blades to turn turbines

% share of world energy consumption less than 1

Main producers Denmark, California USA

Energy uses electricity

✓ **advantages** very clean; no air pollution; small-scale and large-scale schemes possible; cheap to run

X **disadvantages** winds are unpredictable and not constant; visual and noise pollution in quiet, rural areas; many turbines needed to produce sufficient energy

Fact File — Geothermal

Status renewable

Description boreholes can be drilled below ground to use the earth's natural heat; cold water is pumped down, hot water/steam channelled back

% share of world energy consumption less than 1

Main producers Japan, New Zealand, former USSR, Iceland, Hungary

Energy uses electricity, direct heating

✓ **advantages** many potential sites

X **disadvantages** sulphuric gases; expensive to develop; very high temperature can create maintenance problems

Fact File — Biogas/biomass

Status renewable

Description fermented animal or plant waste or crops (e.g. sugar cane); refuse incineration

% share of world energy consumption less than 1

Main producers Brazil, Japan, Germany, Denmark, India

Energy uses ethanol, methane, electricity, heating

✓ **advantages** widely available, especially in LEDCs; uses waste products; can be used at a local level

X **disadvantages** can be expensive to set up; waste cannot be used in other ways, e.g. fertilisers; some pollution

11.4 A nuclear nation
Japan

Only the USA and France have more nuclear power stations than Japan (Source 1). Germany, Sweden and the UK are scrapping plans to build new reactors, Japan on the other hand is building more reactors.

Unlike other nuclear powers who became leading industrial countries over 100 years ago, Japan's industry developed in the twentieth century. Japan has become one of the world's most important industrial nations despite lacking its own energy resources. Although Japan has small amounts of coal, oil and gas, most fossil fuels have to be imported. World oil crises in the 1970s led to sharp price rises. The Japanese are worried about their dependence on other countries – over 99 per cent of their oil is imported. Nuclear power is seen as a cheaper and cleaner alternative to the import and burning of fossil fuels (Source 2).

Today over 9 per cent of Japan's energy needs are met by the nuclear industry. As new reactors are built, this figure is set to rise to 17 per cent (40 per cent of Japan's electricity) by the year 2010 (Source 3). At the same time, oil's share of the energy market should decrease from 58 per cent to 46 per cent.

Source 1	Leading producers of nuclear power	
Country	**Reactors built**	**Proposed**
USA	107	9
France	56	9
former USSR	49	37
Japan	**41**	**14**
UK	37	—
Germany	22	—
Canada	19	3
Sweden	12	—
Spain	9	5
Korea	9	5

There are currently 429 nuclear power stations worldwide in 31 different countries. Two-thirds of them are in the top six countries on this table.

Source 2 Location of Japan's nuclear power stations

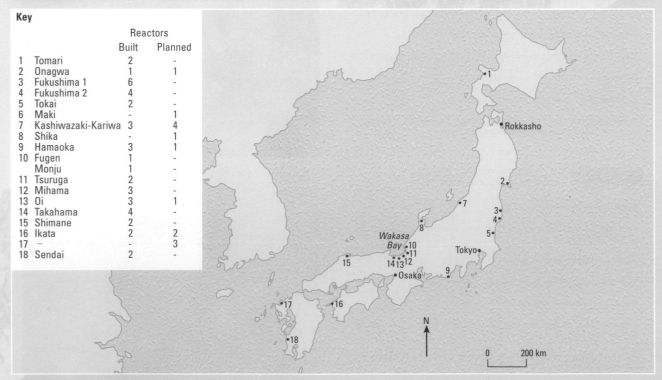

	Reactors	
Key	Built	Planned
1 Tomari	2	-
2 Onagwa	1	1
3 Fukushima 1	6	-
4 Fukushima 2	4	-
5 Tokai	2	-
6 Maki	-	1
7 Kashiwazaki-Kariwa	3	4
8 Shika	-	1
9 Hamaoka	3	1
10 Fugen	1	-
Monju	1	-
11 Tsuruga	2	-
12 Mihama	3	-
13 Oi	3	1
14 Takahama	4	-
15 Shimane	2	-
16 Ikata	2	2
17 –	-	3
18 Sendai	2	-

Japan's first two reactors were built at the end of the 1960s. By 1980 there were 13 reactors. This had risen to 41 by the end of 1991. By the end of the twentieth century there will be 55. Japan has a variety of different types of reactor, but is also experimenting with the newer **fast breeder reactors** (FBRs). This type of reactor uses reprocessed nuclear fuel. This saves on imports since fuel (uranium) used in other Japanese reactors can then be reused. Japan already has a new uranium-enrichment plant and is building a new fuel reprocessing plant.

Good sites for nuclear power stations are in short supply. Flat land and a large water supply are needed. Another important consideration is the stability of the land. Japan experiences over 7000 earthquakes every year and so nuclear power stations must be located in areas safe from potential earthquakes. Pressure on available land has meant that several reactors are often built on the same site. Wakasa Bay has 15 separate reactors around it (Source 4).

| Source 3 | Japan's energy consumption |

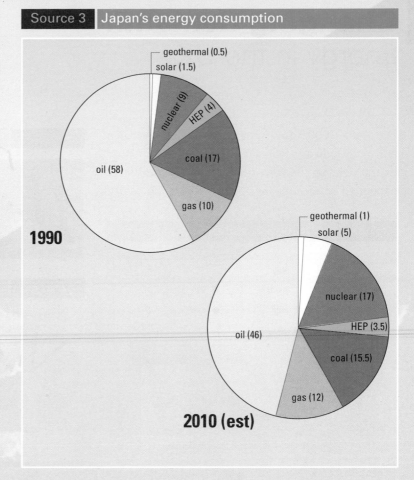

1990

geothermal (0.5)
solar (1.5)
nuclear (9)
HEP (4)
coal (17)
gas (10)
oil (58)

2010 (est)

geothermal (1)
solar (5)
nuclear (17)
HEP (3.5)
coal (15.5)
gas (12)
oil (46)

| Source 4 | Nuclear reactors at Wakasa Bay, Japan |

Despite government enthusiasm, there is increasing opposition to the growth of nuclear power in Japan. A number of pressure groups actively oppose the nuclear programme. Some, like the CNIC (Citizens' Nuclear Information Centre), regularly publish anti-nuclear information. Protests are becoming more common. Concern centres on possible **radiation** leaks and the disposal of nuclear waste. Much of this waste is sent to the UK and France, but Japan is building its own waste plant in the north of Honshu.

Japan may feel that it has little choice but to continue developing its nuclear power industry. However, public opinion is beginning to change. As new technology develops, Japan is in a better position than most countries to develop alternative energy sources such as wind power, solar power and geothermal energy.

Changing demand:
Energy in the UK

The early 1990s saw great changes to the UK's electricity industry, including privatisation. No longer is the UK so heavily dependent on electricity generated in conventional power stations. (Source 1).

Source 1	Coal-fired power station

Source 2	UK power stations

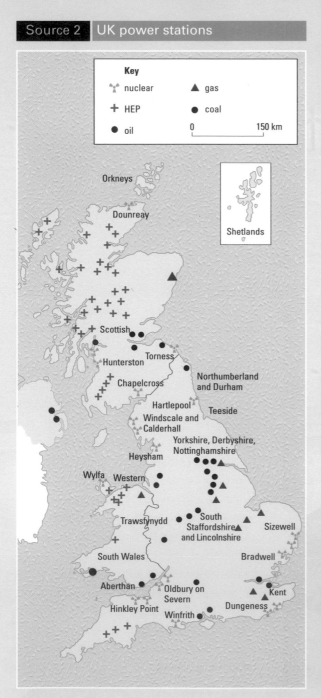

Key
- ☢ nuclear
- ▲ gas
- ＋ HEP
- ● coal
- ● oil

0 150 km

Orkneys

Dounreay

Shetlands

Scottish

Hunterston
Torness

Chapelcross

Northumberland and Durham

Hartlepool
Teeside

Windscale and Calderhall

Yorkshire, Derbyshire, Nottinghamshire

Heysham

Wylfa   Western

Trawsfynydd

South Staffordshire and Lincolnshire

Sizewell

South Wales

Bradwell

Aberthan
Oldbury on Severn

Hinkley Point
Winfrith

Kent

Dungeness

Source 3	UK electricity generation

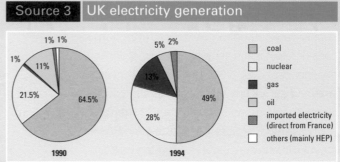

- coal
- nuclear
- gas
- oil
- imported electricity (direct from France)
- others (mainly HEP)

1990: 64.5%, 21.5%, 1%, 11%, 1%, 1%

1994: 49%, 28%, 13%, 5%, 2%

There have also been changes in the relative importance of the energy sources used to generate electricity. Traditionally most electricity in the UK has been produced in thermal power stations burning fossil fuels or by nuclear power reactors (Source 2). However, the pattern is beginning to change (Source 3).

Source 4	Electricity from renewable sources (UK)

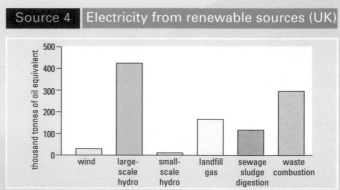

thousand tonnes of oil equivalent

wind, large-scale hydro, small-scale hydro, landfill gas, sewage sludge digestion, waste combustion

Alternative energy sources

At present less than 1% of the UK's energy is produced by alternative sources, such as wind and solar power. Recent Government legislation requires the industry to develop these sources through NFFO (Non Fossil Fuel Obligations) as Source 4 shows.

60 wind projects have been approved in the UK. Electricity is generated by 2 or 3 bladed **turbines**, usually built in groups of 10 to 100 creating **wind farms**. An average wind speed of at least 5 metres per second is needed. The map (Source 1) shows where such conditions are found in the UK. In future up to 10% of the UK's electricity could be generated this way.

Ideal sites for wind farms are often in rural areas. Wind power is clean, but electricity cannot be generated when the wind stops. People are concerned about the noise of the turbines and the visual pollution spoiling large areas of countryside.

Haverigg Wind Farm, Cumbria

The Haverigg Wind Farm (Source 2) is built on a disused airfield at a cost of £1 million. 5 separate 3-bladed wind turbines have been built facing the coast, using the prevailing south-westerly winds. The turbines are each 120 m apart and 30 m high. Power is generated between wind speeds of 3.5 and 25 m/s. At higher wind speeds the turbines are shut down to prevent possible damage. Computers control each turbine, turning the blades to catch the wind.

The wind farm took 2 months to build – access roads were not needed but concrete bases were needed for the turbines. Haverigg began electricity generation in August 1993 and has a life expectancy of 15 years.

| Source 1 | map showing wind farms and possible sites |

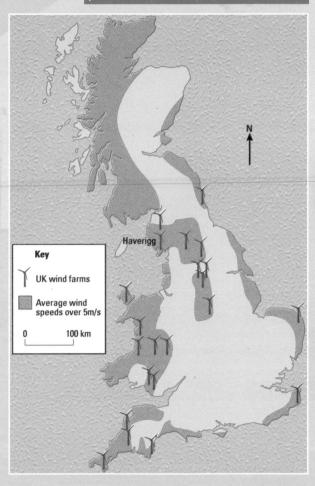

Key

⊥ UK wind farms

▨ Average wind speeds over 5m/s

0   100 km

| Source 2 | Haverigg wind farm |

The benefits of Haverigg Wind Farm are as follows:

- the site is a disused airfield; turbines unlikely to cause objections on the grounds of noise or visual pollution
- a full EIA (Environmental Impact Assessment) was carried out, planning authorities and local people were consulted
- enough electricity is generated per year (3 Gwh) to meet the needs of 500 homes
- local firms were used for construction work, bringing income to the area
- the surrounding farmland can remain in use
- the electricity produced is clean and renewable.

11.7 Energy in Africa:
Fuelwood

Whilst the world's MEDCs are looking to develop alternative energy sources to replace oil, coal and gas, many of the world's LEDCs are suffering from a fuel crisis of their own. 50% of the world's population use wood as their only source of fuel for cooking and heating (Source 1).

The **fuelwood** crisis is especially acute in African countries like Niger and Burkina Faso, south of the Sahara desert in a region known as the Sahel (Source 2). As the population has grown, so has the need to use more wood for cooking. Wood is also cut down to create farmland. As a result, people have to walk further and further from their homes to collect fuelwood as trees close to home have been cut down (Source 3). Trees are being used at such a rate that even replanting programmes cannot keep pace. People often cannot find enough wood and have to find money to buy it. As it becomes even more scarce, prices get higher.

| Source 1 | Fuelwood is gathered on a daily basis |

What can be done?

- More efficient ways of using and managing existing resources are necessary. Improved cooking stoves or ovens, not open fires, would use far less fuel, and lose far less heat.
- Woodland needs to be managed carefully, with new trees replanted to replace those used up.
- If wood is an essential fuel, its other uses e.g. fencing and building need to be met by using alternative materials e.g. wire, bricks etc. Once woodland is removed, bare soil may be lost through erosion and land becomes unproductive.

| Source 2 | The sahel region |

N

Niger   Sahara Desert

20°N

10°N

Burkina Faso

Atlantic Ocean

Key
[ ] The Sahel zone

| Source 3 | Replanting fuelwood cannot keep pace with consumption |

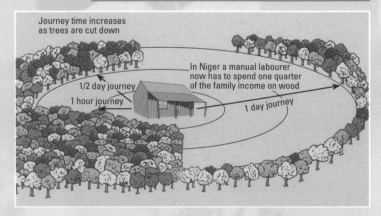

Journey time increases as trees are cut down

In Niger a manual labourer now has to spend one quarter of the family income on wood

1/2 day journey
1 hour journey
1 day journey

Over 85% of Brazil's electricity is generated using hydro-electric power. Using this renewable energy source is important in Brazil, which has little or no fossil fuel deposits of its own. Until recently most HEP stations were built in the south-east of the country (Source 1). However, the Amazonian region in the north-west has great potential for generating HEP.

| Source 1 | Map of the HEP stations in Brazil |

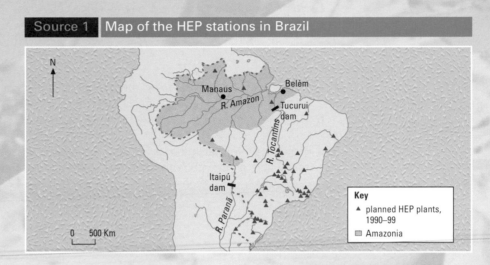

Key
▲ planned HEP plants, 1990–99
▢ Amazonia

The Tucurui Dam, Amazonia

The Tucurui Dam on the River Tocantins, 300 km south of Belem in Northern Brazil (Source 2) was opened in 1985. It was the first large HEP scheme built in the region. It is thought that Amazonia could soon generate up to 40% of Brazil's electricity.

To build the Tucurui Dam, 30 000 people had to move because an area 2 000 km^2 in size was flooded to create the reservoir. Both the flooding and some of the chemicals used to clear the land destroyed plants, animals and land belonging to several tribes of Amazonian Indians. Water in the Tocantins river has become clearer downstream from the dam as silt has been trapped behind it. This makes fishing harder. The changing water levels have also brought increased risk of malaria.

The benefits of the Tucurui Dam are as follows:

- production of cheap electricity from renewable sources
- ability to increase output by adding extra turbines
- industrial development based on the availability of power, for example, bauxite (aluminium) and iron ore, opening up the region
- controlling the flow of the river Tocantins, this helps reduce flooding and improves navigation in the river.

As with most major schemes planned in recent years, an **EIA** (Environment, Impact Assessment) was carried out before the dam was built. However, many people both inside and outside Brazil are concerned that, such schemes will encourage widespread industrialisation in Amazonia, causing immense environmental damage.

| Source 2 | The Tucurui Dam in Brazil |

1 Study Sources 1 and 2 on pages 190–1.
   a Name five of the world's top energy producing countries.
   b Name five of the world's top energy using countries.
   c Are most of these LEDCs or MEDCs? Explain.
   d Look at Source 3, page 191. Make a list of all the different ways energy is being used.

2 a Write definitions for the following energy terms:
      renewable; non-renewable; fossil fuels; alternative energy.
   b What are the main disadvantages of burning fossil fuels?

3 a Using the information on pages 192–5 compile two separate tables – one for non-renewable energy, the other for renewable energy. Use the following headings.

Energy source	Description	Lifespan in years	% of world energy consumption	Uses	Benefits	Disadvantages

   b For each of your completed tables, rank each energy source (best first) by studying the benefits and disadvantages of each energy source and in terms of future importance. Which two sources (one non-renewable, one renewable) come top? (Remember that some factors are more important than others.)

4 'Most non-renewable energy sources cause major environmental problems. Most renewable energy sources are cleaner and better for the environment.'
   Write a short report (250 words) in support of or disagreeing with this statement.

5 List the different factors to be considered when choosing an ideal site for an HEP station.

6 a Using the figures from Source 1 on page 196, draw a pie chart showing the percentage of nuclear power stations found in the top six countries listed. (Note: 'Others' = 27 per cent.)
   b Explain why the Japanese are so determined to decrease their oil imports.
   c What percentage of the world's nuclear reactors are found in Japan?
   d Why do the Japanese often build several reactors on one site?
   e Design a short leaflet, arguing against the development of the nuclear power industry in Japan.

7 a Using Source 1 on page 198, describe and explain the distribution of different types of power stations across the UK.
   b Draw your own map to show the location of the UK's main oil, gas and coal deposits.
   c In 1995 the UK abandoned plans to build new nuclear power stations. Give three reasons for the decision.
   d Research: nuclear power has become an increasingly controversial subject. Organisations like British Electric and BNFL support its use. Pressure groups like Greenpeace and Friends of the Earth are opposed to it. Try to collect literature issued by both sides. Write a script for a debate between representatives of the two sides.

8 Look at Source 1 below.

  a Identify the type of energy which the photograph shows.

  b Is this energy renewable or non-renewable?

  c What is the energy being used for in the photograph?

  d List two advantages and two disadvantages of the type of energy shown.

Source 1	Energy in Cyprus

9 a Use Source 1 on page 199 to make a list of the areas of the UK most suited to the location of new wind farms.

  b Using Source 2 on page 199 make a simple line drawing of one wind turbine. Add labels explaining how it works.

1 World energy resources

Energy is one of the world's most important resources. A wide range of energy resources is found in the natural environment including fossil fuels, uranium, water, sun and wind. MEDCs use a far bigger proportion of the world's energy than LEDCs, despite having a smaller proportion of the world's population. Many MEDCs developed their industries based on the abundance of energy sources.

2 Non-renewable energy sources

Non-renewable energy sources are finite. They are being consumed at ever increasing rates and cannot be replaced.

Fossil fuels are also a major cause of atmospheric pollution. Global warming, the greenhouse effect and acid rain are all caused by burning fossil fuels. Uranium, used in nuclear reactors, produces radiation which can be deadly.

3 Renewable energy sources

Renewable or 'alternative' energy sources are generally cleaner than fossil fuels. Being renewable means they are sustainable sources. At present they supply only 6% of the world's energy needs.

Many renewable sources are in the early stages of development, using new technology, for example, solar power. Other sources, such as wind and water, have been used for centuries.

4 Nuclear Power in Japan

Japan is one of the world's leading nuclear power generators. It has few of its own energy resources and has developed nuclear power rather than depend on imported oil.

The industry has developed rapidly, despite problems in finding suitable safe sites, for example, areas outside earthquake zones. Opposition is growing however, with pressure to develop renewable energy sources.

5 UK energy / wind farms

The UK has traditionally relied on thermal power stations to produce most of its electricity. Gas is taking over from coal and oil as the major fuel. The nuclear industry is stagnating, with no new reactors planned.

The NFFO laws are helping develop alternative energy sources. Wind farms have become widespread in recent years, although they generate less than 1% of the UK's electricity needs.

6 Fuelwood / HEP

Over half the world's population depends on wood for fuel. As resources are used up supply is becoming a major problem. Many now have to find money to buy wood. Cheap alternatives are needed.

Countries like Brazil overcome a lack of fossil fuels by developing hydro-electric power schemes. The Tucurui scheme was the first to be built in Amazonia and may encourage industry to develop in the region.